CIRCUMCISION:
ITS PLACE
IN JUDAISM,
PAST AND PRESENT

Isaac Nathan Publishing Co.
Los Angeles
1998

Comments by clergy and lay readers

"Doctor Kunin's book is a skillful blending of scientific and religious research into the biblical rite of covenant—circumcision that will enrich the reader's understanding of its spiritual and psychological significance. With empathic intelligence it touches upon the relationship between child, parent and the Source of creation. The book punctures the numerous pseudo-scientific biases against circumcision.

Written with a balance of humor and erudition, this book will be of special interest to parents, physicians and rabbis. It anticipates the kinds of questions that families have in preparing for the sacred event of the Brit milah. I entusiastically recommend reading Doctor Kunin's book."

—*Rabbi Harold M. Schulweis,*
Valley Beth Sholom, Encino CA
author of *For Those Who Can't Believe*

"This superb and comprehensive book provides a keen and appreciative understanding of *Brit milah*. Easy to read and grasp, Doctor Kunin relieves parental concern about this basic Jewish rite, affirms our historic commitment to the oldest rite in Judaism.

All religious and surgical aspects of the Brit are considered in a pleasant literary style. It introduces the modern *mohel*, blessed with medical skills and dedicated to the preservation of basic Jewish values.

The book combines medical information and religious enlightenment which promises to become a classic."

—*Rabbi Harry Essrig,*
Publisher of *The American Rabbi*

"Sam Kunin is a knowledgeable doctor, an enthusiastic Jew, and a real *mensch:* all three of these qualities come together in this book which will be of great value to many parents and will help make *Brit milah* meaningful and sacred to many."

—*Rabbi Jack Riemer,*
Congregation Beth Tikvah, Boca Raton, FL.,
Co-editor of *So Your Values Live On.,*
Chair of the National Rabbinic Network

"Doctor Kunin has written a marvelous little book which could have been named, '*All You Ever Wanted to Know About a Brit.*' In well organized chapters, every aspect of the subject is covered succinctly, logically and to the point. This book should be required reading for every expectant Jewish parent since the possibility of having a newborn son is 50%."

—*Rabbi Isaiah Zeldin,*
Stephen S. Wise Temple, Los Angeles, CA
author of *What This Modern Jew Believes*

"Dr Kunin has written a thorough, unsqueamish and helpful guide for families facing the powerful, but daunting, *mitzvah* of *Brit milah.*" — *Anita Diamant,*
author of *The New Jewish Baby Book,*
The Jewish Weddings, and *Choosing a Jewish Life.*

"This is wonderful! It provides a lot of important information in an easily understandable style that is also friendly and inviting."

—*Rabbi Elliot Dorff,*
Rector and Professor of Philosophy,
University of Judaism, Los Angeles
Author of: *Matters of Life & Death:*
A Jewish Approach to Bio-Ethics

"Finally, a book that covers the medical aspects of circumcision accurately and the religious and social aspects thoughtfully and honestly. I wish this book had been available when my son asked me about circumcising his son."

—*Doctor Arthur Ulene*
Nationally Syndicated Television Medical Commentator

"This book is a welcome response to the myths, misconceptions, and misinformation surrounding the issue of circumcision."

—*Laura C. Schlessinger, Ph.D.*
Internationally syndicated radio talk-show host
Author of: *How Could You Do That?!*
The Abdication of Character, Courage and Conscience

"I heartily recommend this book!"

—*Dennis Prager*
Syndicated radio talk show host and lecturer
author of *Happiness is a Serious Problem:*
A Human Nature Repair Manual

CIRCUMCISION:
ITS PLACE
IN JUDAISM,
PAST AND PRESENT

By Samuel A. Kunin, M.D.

Edited by David W. Epstein

Isaac Nathan Publishing Co., Inc.

Los Angeles

1998

1st. Printing, March 1998

Library of Congress Cataloging-in-Publication Data

Samuel A. Kunin, M.D.

Circumcision

1. Judaism   2. Jewish Practices

3. Circumcision   4. Jewish Rituals

ISBN 0-914615-07-6

Library of Congress Catalog Card Number: 98-65302

Manufactured in the United States of America

Isaac Nathan Publishing Co., Inc.
22711 Cass Avenue
Woodland Hills, California, 91364

Telephone:	(818) 225-9631
FAX	(818) 225-8354
e-mail	david@inpubco.com
Website:	www.inpubco.com

CONTENTS

✡

Acknowledgements

So many to thank...so little space!

My deepest appreciation and thanks to:

Rabbi Steven B. Jacobs—for suggesting I become a *mohel* and Dr. Lewis Barth who directed my training as a *mohel*.

Rabbi Harold Schulweis—my spiritual guide, who reviewed this book.

Rabbi Edward Feinstein—who invited me to lecture to rabbinical students at the University of Judaism in Los Angeles, where I was able to create a forum for many of the ideas presented in this book.

Rabbi Elliot Dorff—who reviewed this book and provided materials regarding legal issues in Conservative Judaism.

Rabbi Neil Weinberg and all of the dedicated rabbis at the University of Judaism conversion program and at the *mikvah*.

Lillian Zelcer Rosenbloom—the "*mikvah* lady."

Rabbi Haskell Bernat—who brought me to task on checking facts and providing a proper scholarly approach in his review of this book.

Ilene Gelbaum, CNM and *mohelet*—a wonderful "forum" for techniques and counters to the anti-circumcision movement.

Dolly Edmonds and Norma Harris—for their professional criticism.

Rabbi Isaiah Zeldin, Rabbi Jack Reimer, Rabbi Harry Essrig, Rabbi Gordon Bernat-Kunin, Dennis Prager, Dr. Laura Schlessinger, Doctor Art Ulene and Doctor Edgar Schoen—who were also kind enough read the galleys and lend their expertise.

The first step taken to create a first book is a difficult one. Gentle shoves, creative insights, parachutes and encouragement were provided—for the past four years—by my friend and editor/publisher David W. Epstein of Isaac Nathan Publishing Co., Inc.

I owe my family a great debt of gratitude. Had he only brought us Dina, his wife, mother of Gavriella Ayelet and Yonah Gershon, *dayanu*—it would have been enough, but My oldest son, Rabbi Gordon Bernat-Kunin has also been my teacher of Bible and Rabbinics at his *beit midrash*. Douglas, my second son and Nathalie, his wife provided me with the thrill of circumcising my first grandson, Ethan David. Kenneth, my youngest son, helps me run the business part of my work and Kathy, his wife completes a wonderful family.

Life for me, without my other (and better) half, would be incomplete. I find my "wholeness" with Nancy, my beloved wife. She has the patience of an angel, and she needed every ounce of it, to proof-read this book, again and again.

Samuel A. Kunin, M.D.
Los Angeles, California
March, 1998, Adar, 5758

Foreward . . . .

by the Chairman of the American Pediatric Association Task Force on Circumcision.

As both a practicing urologist and a committed Jew, Doctor Kunin is in a unique position to present both the medical and religious aspects of newborn circumcision. Having performed more than 5,000 circumcisions without any significant complications, Doctor Kunin presents an example of the safety of the procedure in skilled hands, as well as indicating the deep religious significance of a rite that has been a key part of Judaism since the time of Abraham.

By asking and answering a series of questions, Doctor Kunin addresses medical and religious concerns of parents and health professionals alike. What is the difference between Orthodox, Conservative, and Reform rituals? How is the infant restrained? What is done in unusual situations such as the case of twins or the existence of penile abnormalities?

Of special interest is the fact that local anesthesia is permitted under religious law and is used by Doctor Kunin. This advance favors the choice of a physician *mohel* rather than a certified lay *mohel* who is limited to either no anesthesia or to ointments, rather than to the more effective local injection, although the sweet wine which the infant sucks has a proven pain-relieving effect.

Anti-circumcision activists have influenced intellectual, secular Jews, particularly on the East and West coasts. Today there is some justification to state that a newborn baby is more likely to be circumcised if he is born a Methodist in rural Wisconsin than a Jew in Berkeley. Perhaps Doctor Kunin's valuable experience, along with increasing medical evidence of the preventive health benefits of newborn circumcision, will change this trend.

This book is recommended for not only Jewish physicians and parents, but for all who are interested in the medical and religious basis of this ancient and rich tradition.

—Edgar J. Schoen, MD
Senior Consultant in Pediatrics
Kaiser Permanente Medical Care Program, Oakland, CA
Clinical Professor of Pediatrics,, University of California, San Francisco

Chapter One

WHY WRITE A BOOK ABOUT CONTEMPORARY CIRCUMCISION AND BRIT MILAH?

Introduction

I am a Board Certified Urologic Surgeon, in practice since 1966. In 1984, the Hebrew Union College-Jewish Institute of Religion in Los Angeles, and the *Berit Milah* Board*, under the directorship of Dr. Lewis Barth, rabbi and dean of HUC-JIR, convened the first class of physicians and nurses trained to be non-Orthodox *mohalim/ot*—ritual circumcisers. I was part of that class and have been a practicing *mohel* in the Southern California area ever since.

This has allowed me to blend together three things I dearly love—Judaism, surgery and teaching. Most of my time is spent counseling people on both the religious and surgical aspects of *Brit milah*. I often lecture on *Brit milah* in synagogues, schools and Jewish community centers. At the University of Judaism in Los Angeles, besides teaching rabbinical students, I volunteer my services for the conversion program at the *mikvah*—ritual bath. For this particular work I have been awarded, in 1998, the *Community Service Award* by the Rabbinical Assembly—(Organization of Conservative Rabbis).

This book has been written so individuals and couples will have both a Jewish-religious and a 20/21st century scientific understanding of the ritual of circumcision.

---

* The are many ways to transliterate a Hebrew word. We use *Brit milah*. However, when citing other books or organizations, we use their choice.

Brit Milah—Covenant of circumcision—is introduced in the Hebrew Bible in the *Book of Genesis,* chapter 17. The only mandates listed are that circumcision is to be performed; and that it must be done on the eighth day after the birth of a male child. There is no mention of how it should be performed, who must be present, or what prayers should be said.

Today's *Brit milah* traditions are the result of a great deal of interpretation through the ages. There have been many changes, often paralleling dominant religious ideas brought on by external political, social, economic and now scientific factors.

While the religious aspects of the ceremony have changed, the medical practice of circumcision has also evolved. It is difficult today to perceive how Abraham circumcised himself almost four thousand years ago.

In contrast to ancient practices, contemporary medicine often offers a variety of treatments for any one particular condition. A doctor often chooses one of many treatments available, and the patient usually accepts it. However, when it comes to circumcision, an inflexibility exists which has sparked debates about both the religious and medical aspects of *Brit milah.*

To varying degrees, most Jews look to Orthodoxy for measuring Jewish identity and authenticity. Consider the *kosher* laws. Without Orthodox approval, a *kosher* restaurant can be closed or a product boycotted into extinction. I can walk into any Reform or Conservative synagogue gift shop and find a candelabra, *challah* cover, seder plate or some other Judaica with pictures of dancing Chassids seemingly lending their seal of authentic Jewishness. And yet these same non-Orthodox institutions were formed in response to Jews who wanted change from that same Orthodoxy.

Judaism has always been a living, vital, changing religion and while the non-Orthodox acknowledge the Orthodox, the opposite is not always so. Current Orthodoxy does not recognize non-Orthodox conversion, therefore creating potential challenges to any non-Orthodox *Brit milah*. These challenges arise at many levels, including:

1. which mothers are considered to be Jewish,

2. who is eligible for a *Brit*,

3. who can perform the *Brit*, and

4. what methods can be utilized.

This process of selection can become very complex.

In an Orthodox community, life with its complex decisions can be relatively easy. If I were writing this book about *Brit milah* for their community, a number of chapters would be omitted. Defending the benefits of circumcision would be unnecessary because not circumcising would be out of the question. What types of clamps to be used and whether or not to administer anesthesia might be of interest, but are essentially non-issues.

No explanation would be needed as to why circumcision is done early on the eighth day. It is expected. Discussion about egalitarian blessings, gay and lesbian families, patrilineal descent or single parent *Britot* would not be welcomed.

However, I do not live or function in that world and I suspect that most reading this book live as I do. I live in a more liberal, modern Jewish world; a highly complex world composed of many divisions. My Jewish world consists of Conservative, Reconstructionist and Reform, which have within themselves wide variations ranging from traditional to liberal. And then for good measure, it also must include all the non-affiliated members of the Jewish community.

These variations in Judaism have evolved because we are a people who constantly asks questions and often finds different answers. On Passover we ask four questions, but when it comes to circumcision and *Brit milah,* we don't stop at four. (I should be so lucky!) As a *mohel,* I have been confronted with countless questions about both *halachic*—Jewish legal—and medical issues. I have spent thousands of hours answering the questions when I could, or researching the answers.

This book is an attempt to present the most frequently asked questions with their answers, presenting contemporary, liberal Jewish as well as modern medical viewpoints.

✡

Chapter Two

WHAT IS BRIT MILAH ?

WHAT ARE THE JEWISH ORIGINS OF BRIT?

IS A BRIT A JEWISH "BAPTISM"?

The Hebrew words *Brit* and *milah* mean "covenant" and "circumcision." *Webster's New Collegiate Dictionary* defines a covenant as more than just a contract. It is a solemn and binding agreement, or a promise between two or more persons for the performance of some action. Circumcision is defined as the removal of the male foreskin or prepuce. *Brit milah* thus becomes the "covenant of circumcision."

The ceremony is primarily derived from the *Book of Genesis*, chapter 17. Prior to this passage God has promised Avram and Sarai that countless generations will flow from them. In *Genesis 17*, Avram is 99 years old and Sarai is 90. God tells Avram that if he circumcises himself and all of the males in his household, Sarai will finally have a baby. Hearing this, Avram laughs, as does Sarai in *Genesis 19*. Much is made of this laughter in later commentaries, some suggesting people will laugh at her for being 90 and pregnant and others at the thought of Avram becoming a father at 100.

However, Avram has faith and circumcises himself, Ishmael—his 13 year old son from Hagar, Sarai's handmaiden—and every male member of his household. From that moment on, Avram is known as Abraham, the father of mighty nations and Sarai as Sarah, the princess of these nations.

In her 90's, Sarah gives birth to a child who is named Isaac, meaning "he will laugh." This reminds us of Abraham's and Sarah's earlier laughter.

All of this leads us to the eighth day of Isaac's life when the Covenant of circumcision begins. God makes the following pact with Abraham: if Abraham circumcises Isaac on the eighth day and teaches Isaac to circumcise his son on the eighth day and this Covenant is continued throughout the generations, God will assure that Abraham's lineage will be fruitful, multiplying like the stars in the heavens and Canaan will always be their homeland. The circumcision will forever be a sign of this Covenant between God and Abraham.

For nearly four thousand years this contract has been renewed by Jews even when doing so was punishable by death. It holds such significance that even Spinoza, the seventeenth century Jewish philosopher said, "The sign of circumcision is . . . so important . . . it alone would preserve the nation forever."

Our great Rabbi Akiba, on facing death, was asked by the Roman, Tinneaus Rufus, "If your God is so great, why are you not born circumcised?" Akiba replied that God creates wheat and man makes bread. His answer affirmed that Jews are here to complete God's work on earth and implied that a male child is not complete until circumcised. (Of course, the corollary is that girls are born perfect.)

The *Brit milah* ceremony that has evolved through the centuries includes the circumcision on the eighth day and the giving of the child's Hebrew name with appropriate blessings. There is no biblical instruction regarding the procedure to be utilized for the circumcision. The blessings and service evolved later.

When my sons became *b'nai mitzvah*, we were encouraged to write creative services. We were given the basic core of blessings that must be included and encouraged to augment them with any prayers, readings or songs that we thought were significant.

And so it is with contemporary *Brit milah*. Attend an Orthodox *brit* and you will probably experience the basic core of prayers with little added, as it has been done for centuries. However, *Brit milah* is thousands of years old, so we can be sure that it has been, and is still evolving.

Contemporary Jews have chosen to make what has been a mysterious and often frightening ceremony into a warm, understandable, educational and even user-friendly experience.

I am often asked if a *Brit* is a Jewish form of baptism. From an historical standpoint *Brit milah* precedes baptism by over two thousand years. Therefore, I suggest that the question would be better stated as, "Is a baptism a Christian brit?" But, no matter how the question is phrased, there is no similarity in the two events.

Christians consider the newborn infant to be born with "original sin." Baptism is an external rite which exorcises this Satanic influence. The priest blows on the child's face and orders Satan away. The parents are asked to renounce Satan. Infants who die without a baptism are denied heaven.

When a child is brought into the room for a *Brit milah* everyone rises to honor him. This is because the infant is born *b'tzelem Elohim*—in the image of God. Judaism assumes that every child is born with a pure soul.

✡

Chapter Three
WHAT IS A CIRCUMCISION ?

The basic definition of a circumcision is the surgical removal of the foreskin or prepuce—the sleeve of skin that covers the glans penis—the 'head of the penis.' This section of skin may vary greatly from partially covering the glans to extending far beyond it.

The foreskin is rarely, if ever, absent at birth. I have never personally witnessed such an occurrence. In some societies its absence would suggest the birth of someone who is very special. Some commentaries have suggested that both Moses and King David were *noldu mahulim*—born circumcised. Another says that Adam was born circumcised and that after he was expelled from the Garden of Eden, his foreskin grew back. Muslims believe that Mohammed was born circumcised, and some African tribes consider such individuals to be blessed.

In Judaism, we believe that by circumcising an infant, we are completing God's work and rendering the child perfect and entering him into the Covenant of Abraham.

Much speculation occurs as to the origin of circumcision, a practice that has even been depicted in ancient cave paintings. A Bible fundamentalist believes that, following excision of a rib, circumcision was the second surgical procedure in history.

From a more scientific viewpoint we know that some mummies were circumcised and ancient Egyptian paintings confirm this practice that would pre-date Abraham.

Circumcision is currently practiced by one sixth of the world's population. All of Islam circumcises males, but usually at a later age, because, as we noted earlier, Ishmael was circumcised at thirteen years. African tribes are known to circumcise as a rite of passage into manhood. In the well-known book *Roots,* by Alex Haley, Kunta Kinta goes through such a ritual.

Australian Aborigines, ancient Aztecs and Mayans, North and South American Indians and some island people in both the Pacific and Indian oceans did, or still circumcise. All Phillipine Catholic boys are currently circumcised between eight to ten years of age. This is a somewhat unusual practice since many fundamentalist Christians circumcise their children at eight days of age because that is when Jesus was circumcised. Perhaps the Phillipine practice is a result of the merger of an older tradition with the newer practice of Christianity. Most non-Christian Filipinos do not circumcise, nor do Christians in Europe and South America.

We may have found some clues to the origin of circumcision in the World War II North African experience and later with Operation Desert Storm. In both campaigns, balanitis—infection of the foreskin—was a significant problem. The combination of heat, sand and infrequent bathing probably led to this condition. It was also a problem in the South Pacific during World War II and, as a result, the most frequent ship-board operation was circumcision.

As a U.S. Navy urologist assigned to the Marines at Camp Pendleton, California, during the Viet Nam war, not a week passed that I was not asked to circumcise marines who were preparing to go to Viet Nam. Stories of 'jungle rot' of the penis were common and these marines did not want to take any chances.

Understanding this, let us go back to the days of Pharoah's court in Egypt. Speculate that either Pharoah or someone of importance in his court had a severe infection of his foreskin with all of its attendant problems—painful erections, local pain and bleeding. The court physician was called in. He tried prayers, incantations, potions, and lotions, all to no avail. We know physicians of that time had some surgical instruments—a knife and even tools for drilling holes into skulls. He could perform one of two operations with his knife, either amputation or lancing for incision and drainage. Some of these surgeons were particularly skilled at removing bladder stones through an incision in the perineum, an area between the scrotum and anus.

The surgeon must have thought, "If I amputate Pharoah's penis, whether it works or not, I'm in big trouble. I think I'll try incision and drainage first." And, fortunately, it worked!

In the famous book by T.H. White called *The Once and Future King*, which later became the hit musical *Camelot*, they speak (and sing) of things that are "too good for the common folks" and that's probably how it was for circumcision in ancient Egypt. It was only offered to people of status or wealth.

Judaism introduced circumcision to all males in our community at infancy—an act of equality and nobility.

✡

Chapter Four
WHAT MAKES A CIRCUMCISION "KOSHER"?
WHAT TYPES OF CLAMPS ARE USED?

" Jews are extreme optimists. They cut off ten per cent of the penis before
they even know how long it is going to be."

I have heard this crude joke more times than I can remember.
In a way, it conjures up all of the fears about circumcision—
particularly in men. Of course the joke misstates the definition.
None of the penis is cut off. Only foreskin is removed.

A circumcision is considered "kosher" when it is performed
at the correct time (page 36), by an appropriate person (pages 65
and 84), in a prescribed manner. This chapter deals with the
latter.

In defining the components of a "kosher" circumcision, we
must consider three distinct parts of the procedure:

1. *Milah,* the removal of the *orla* or foreskin, the actual circum-
    cision.

2. *Periah,* the freeing up of the foreskin surrounding the glans
    —head of the penis—so the glans is exposed. A circumci-
    sion is not considered "kosher" unless the head of the penis
    is exposed.

3. *Metzitzah,* the drawing of blood from the circumcision
    wound because a *brit* may not be bloodless.

(It is hard to believe that this ancient custom is still done by mouth in parts of the world today, including the U.S.A. It obviously should not be done for two reasons; hepatitis and HIV. At one *brit* I performed, the family told me about a child in the 'old country' who died from sepsis—a systemic infection— because the *mohel* had a gum infection.)

Today, some *mohalim* use a glass pipette (like a medicine dropper) to satisfy this requirement. The Reform movement does not require *metzitzah*, but I always show a drop or two of blood on a gauze sponge, which fulfills the requirement.

There is agreement regarding the above components. However, some controversy occurs regarding what instruments may be used for the circumcision. Either a shield or clamp is used. The type of clamp has been, and remains the focus of these discussions.

The more traditional will argue that a *brit* may not be done with any clamp. They claim that a clamp creates pain and devitalizes the tissue so that there may not be the required drops of blood. Therefore, they only use a Mogen shield, a device through which they pull up and then remove the foreskin. They depend on the bandage to control bleeding. The potential for severe bleeding is greater with this procedure and is one reason for the invention of clamps.

Clamps seal the skin, reducing the risk of infection and bleeding. Therefore *mohalim* who still use the shield will often use a bandage soaked with epinephrine in order to constrict blood vessels and stop the bleeding. The use of epinephrine is not without risk because it increases the heart rate. Still this technique is considered "kosher" by some, whereas the use of clamps is not.

Why? There is no biblical explanation as to how Abraham circumcised himself or Isaac. Knives, shields, clamps, dressings and epinephrine are not mentioned. I doubt if they were even mentioned when the Oral Laws were given at Mount Sinai.

If modern science can provide techniques that reduce pain, greatly diminish bleeding and infection, and avoid complications, how, in good conscience, can modern *mohalim* ignore them?

Before continuing this discussion, allow me another story:

A rabbi was working in his office at the synagogue when torrential rains started a flood. He climbed to the roof and waited. As the floodwaters rose to the roof line, a row boat came by with members of the synagogue who called out, "Rabbi, please come with us now. The flood is getting worse."

He replied, "No thanks. You go on. God will save me."

As the waters rose to his waist level, another boat came by and the rescuers pleaded with him to get in the boat. Again he replied, "No thank you. God will save me."

With the waters now reaching his neck, a helicopter flew by and the rescue team called down, "Rabbi, please—we beg you—let us drop you a line so you can come with us to safety."

As before, he called out, "No thank you. God will save me."

He drowns and when he reaches heaven, he confronts God and says, "God! I told everyone you would save me and look what happened. Why didn't you come to save me?"

God answers, "What are you talking about? I sent you two boats and a helicopter!"

This story suggests that one way God works is by giving us the ability to develop techniques and methods that allow us to help ourselves. We are partners with God and, to that end, we are obligated to use our God-given abilities.

In 1934 the Gomco clamp was introduced by two physicians—Aaron Goldstein, M.D. and Hiram Yellin, M.D.— and started a new era in circumcision. Although many other clamps have evolved since then, many hold the opinion that this is still the best clamp ever devised, setting standards for safety, prevention of excessive bleeding and cosmetic results. This clamp has come to be known as "The Doctors' clamp."

The one mistake made in introducing this clamp was that it was labeled as a "bloodless clamp." Obviously from the requirements listed above, if it were true, the Gomco clamp could not be used for ritual circumcisions. This clamp though, is far from bloodless. Having used it for over thirty years, I have never failed to produce the required drops of blood.

The Plastibell is a variant of the Gomco clamp and is quite effective. However, some physicians and parents elect not to use it because the plastic "bell" remains attached to the penis for up to a week. There is no discomfort during this time.

In 1945, possibly in answer to the Gomco clamp, Rabbi Aaron Bronstein introduced what has come to be known generically as the Mogen clamp. Although it is considered to be "The *Mohels'* clamp," it is often used by physicians. This clamp is quicker, easier to learn how to use, less expensive, and requires less maintenance. He modified a Mogen shield hinging the closed end and placing a clamping mechanism over the open end. He also created a curved groove on the side nearest the penis to prevent injury to the head of the penis. Circumcision, with the Mogen clamp or the Mogen shield, is a blind procedure in that the foreskin is separated with a finger nail or probe before removing the foreskin. The head of the penis is not seen until after the circumcision.

Contrast that with a Gomco clamp which is applied under direct vision with the aid of a dorsal slit , a small incision on the top of the foreskin, which allows visual freeing up of the membranes. The glans penis and the urethra are inspected to assure no hidden congenital anomalies. The "bell," a thimble-like device which completely protects the head of the penis is applied before the circumcision.

The dorsal slit is another point of contention because if ultra-traditional Jews reject the clamp, they will obviously not tolerate an extra incision. It is interesting that by far, the majority of Orthodox *mohalim* use the Mogen clamp, and—continuing the 'holier than thou' discourse—they reject the Gomco clamp. This suggests a "clamp hierarchy," the shield being holier than a Mogen clamp which is holier than a Gomco clamp.

However, even for those who do not use the Gomco clamp normally, there are sound medical reasons for using it for specific anatomical situations, including:

1. a small or thin penis,
2. children with a lot of fat in the area or with large scrotums due to fat or scrotal lesions like hydroceles; and
3. children with scant skin on the scrotal side due to webbing of the skin.

This very point was made by Elliot Leiter, M.D., a urologist lecturing to Orthodox *mohalim* at the *Fifth Brith Milah Board In-Service Training* at the Mount Sinai School of Medicine. So does one selectively use the Gomco clamp in only these situations? Can a clamp be a "little bit kosher?" If it is good for one particular situation, why is it not good for all?

I think Dr. Lewis Barth, rabbi and dean at Hebrew Union College-Jewish Institute of Religion in Los Angeles, stated the case for clamps best when he said that religiosity is not conveyed through clamps, but through those applying them.

Today, controversy continues between *mohalim* who defend their beliefs and techniques. In general, the belief determines the technique. Orthodox *mohalim* make their choice based on their interpretation of Jewish Law. Physician-*mohalim* make their choice based their medical training. Both groups tend to protect their biases.

I, too, have a particular bias, based on what I believe to be considerable scientific evidence, but in no way do I want to lead you to believe there is only one correct way to perform a circumcision.

For thousands of years, millions of circumcisions have been performed satisfactorily with a variety of techniques including flint stones, conch shells and almost anything imaginable. Properly trained *mohalim* can obtain optimum results with any of these contemporary procedures.

From a non-Orthodox perspective, expertise with any clamp will provide a satisfactory "kosher" result. I've always assumed that there are enough foreskins to go around.

✡

Chapter Five
ARE YOU GOING TO USE A BOARD?

Of course, I use a board. Consider the options. Traditionally, the *sandak*—the person with the honor of holding the child during the circumcision—sits with the baby on a pillow on his lap or on a table. The baby's head is pointed to the *sandak*. The *sandak* holds the baby's legs at the knees so the legs will be straight. The *sandak's* forearms are positioned over the baby's arms so that the arms and legs are immobilized. The *sandak* is looking directly at the circumcision all the time, unless he chooses to close his eyes. If he becomes ill or squeamish he could conceivably loosen his grip.

Contrast that with the board that is most often used in hospitals, called the Olympic Circumstraint. It is plastic and molded to the shape of the baby's body. There is an elevated portion between the legs so that any clamp can rest on it without any tension to the penis. There are cut-out places for Velcro straps on the sides to secure the arms and legs.

Years ago, at a convention of *mohalim*, I learned it was not necessary to strap the arms. Since then, I never tie down the child's arms but I loosely secure his legs so he will not kick or slip off during the procedure. The results were startling. The babies cry less and are able to interact with the people around them, sometimes grasping a finger or searching for their own mouths or touching the wine and sugar-soaked cloth they are being offered. Since then, I have done thousands of circumcisions, and no baby has ever reached down where I am working.

There are other boards. I have seen an Orthodox *mohel* fashion a similar restraint on a straight, padded board with arm and leg restraints both being used. This board was placed on the *sandak's* lap. He covered it up so well I seriously doubt that anyone knew he was using it since he had the *sandak's* back to the audience. Actually, any of these boards work well.

Personally, I would rather use a board than have someone hold the baby. The board suits the way I do the *brit*, preparing the baby beforehand and then bringing him into the room. Other *mohalim* have their own techniques. The *mohel* should use whatever technique makes him or her and the baby comfortable.

✡

Chapter Six

IS AN ANESTHETIC PERMITTED AT BRIT MILAH ?

WHAT TYPES OF ANESTHETIC ARE THERE ?
CAN WE FEED THE BABY BEFORE THE BRIT ?
IS IT TRUE THAT THE BABY CAN GET DRUNK ?

When considering the use of anesthesia for a *Brit milah,* it seems hard to believe that there would be any opposition to easing any pain. The commandment is to perform the circumcision. There is no provision that the child has to experience pain.

It is fascinating to learn that using sweet grape wine, as we have done for thousands of years, has a sound medical basis. The baby is sedated from the sugar in the sweet wine rather than made drunk from the alcohol. Many *mohalim,* including me, add water to the wine in order to dilute the alcohol, and I add granulated sugar to increase the sugar concentration.

Let us dismiss any thoughts that the baby does not feel anything during a circumcision. Some have said that the nerve endings are not well developed. Even if they are not, studies measuring blood pressure, heart rate and the chemical cortisol show that all three of these parameters of pain response go up during circumcision. When a concentrated sugar solution is given to the child before and during the procedure, all three measurements go down, suggesting that sugar is a sedative in a newborn child. This is the opposite effect of the "sugar high" experienced in children at later ages. There is also evidence that the sugar releases natural pain fighters through endorphin stimulation. This is the reason we use an inexpensive sweet Concord grape wine. It is important to impress this upon parents, but occasionally there are wine afficionados who must buy a fine dry wine. Please save the good wine for the guests. The baby needs the sweet wine.

Occasionally, when the child is given full strength wine, he will develop more mucous and be inclined to spit up more often. That is another reason I dilute the wine with water and add granulated sugar when creating the baby's first "cocktail." This concoction drastically reduces the incidence of spitting up.

In those homes where alcohol is not consumed, grape juice is totally appropriate and the blessing for the "fruit of the vine"—*boray p're hagafen*—may still be said.

There is nothing more distressing than a baby spitting up during the ceremony. Therefore, most *mohalim* follow the guidelines established by almost every hospital nursery—namely that the baby should not eat one hour before his circumcision. I ask the mother to feed her son an hour and a half before the *brit,* allowing a half-hour for feeding. After one hour, most babies will not cry because of hunger. Their stomachs have started to empty and they will tolerate and absorb the "cocktail." If the baby is crying because of hunger during that hour, one can safely give him a *nasch,* just enough to take the edge off.

In discussing anesthetic agents, I mention topical sprays like those used at athletic events, only to dismiss them. They work by "freezing" the involved area. This can be uncomfortable for the child, and any minimal gain achieved is offset by the risk of sensitizing the infant skin to the ingredients in the spray and the subsequent swelling and redness that may occur. They don't work that well anyway.

Lidocaine is the active agent in both creams and injections. There is a topical cream called EMLA cream—Eutectic Mixture of Local Anesthetics—that is now being used by some *mohalim*. I prefer not to use it for the following reasons:

1. Although used for circumcisions, it is not approved by the FDA for this use in babies under thirty days of age.

2. It is expensive. The cost of a prescription may be as much as ten times the cost of a local injection.

3. It has to be applied, by the parents, 45 to 60 minutes before the procedure. It works very well on flat surfaces where the cream has to be covered with an occlusive dressing in order to get the skin to "sweat" and for the lidocaine to be absorbed. However, there is no satisfactory way to wrap the penis. The dressing provided with the cream is often ineffective. Some use plastic wrap, and I have tried a finger cot with a hole in the end for urination.

4. Since the parents have to apply the cream, and penises vary in size, it is difficult to determine an accurate dose.

5. There is a known side effect called an "irritable focus" which occurs in over half of the children. Often children will cry much harder and longer after using EMLA than if nothing was given except for some wine or sugar. This is due to an "irritable focus" which is similar to what we feel when we go to the dentist and feel the numbness and tingling sensation that occurs as anesthetic wears off. It is

not pain. Infants only have two forms of communication, tears and silence. When they feel this new and strange sensation, they can only tell us with tears. It may last as long as 30 to 45 minutes. When EMLA works without this side effect it is effective.

However, since the latest studies all state that EMLA works, "almost as well as an injection of lidocaine," why not use what works best? Local injection for circumcision has been used for years. The first form of anesthesia was a dorsal penile nerve block or DPNB. Some mistakes were made during its early use. It got a bad reputation because of (1.) hematoma—a swelling of blood below the skin, (2.) the block not working, or (3.) convulsions caused by injection of the lidocaine into the spongy bodies of the penis, called corpora. Obviously, many shied away from DPNB. However, when used properly, it is an excellent and safe form of anesthesia. Doctors who don't know how to use it tend to berate it, and non-medical *mohalim* who may not administer it without a license are quick to criticize its use.

There are two other forms of injection available:

1. A subcutaneous "ring block" of lidocaine at the base of the penis. This technique was described by Edward Drenth, M.D. and Richard S. Hurwitz, M.D. They used it on 2,278 patients circumcised at Kaiser Foundation Hospital in Los Angeles, California. There is no potential for deep injection of lidocaine into the *corpora* and it works almost instantaneously. It is given through one injection site at the base of the penis with good control of the administered dose. The one potential complication of this, as with any administration of lidocaine, is the possibility of an irritable focus. Studies have shown the "ring block" to be more effective than DPNB or EMLA cream.

2. Local injection at the tip of the foreskin. In an attempt to avoid the irritable focus, I inject lidocaine below the skin near the tip of the penis where most of the clamping and manipulation will be done. Much less anesthetic agent is needed, and this technique works as well as any of the methods listed above. When the foreskin is removed, so is the lidocaine that was injected into this portion of skin. As with all anesthetic techniques, there may be some crying, but there are enough benefits to consider this method. It is particularly suited for a chubby baby with a short penis since there is less distortion of the skin during the circumcision.

As much information as possible about anesthesia should be given to parents so that they may make an informed decision. The decision best for the baby is reached when both the parents and the *mohel* are flexible.

In concluding, you should know that many parents reject the use of anesthesia for a variety of reasons. Some don't like the potential side effects or the thought of giving an injection. Some have had boys circumcised before and felt that since there were no previous problems, why change a good thing.

Whether or not anesthesia is given, sucking some form of sugar solution is always indicated. Other modalities which may help include; swaddling, talking or singing to the baby in soft tones, and staying relaxed. Babies seem to sense when people are tense around them.

Studies show that acetaminophen (Tylenol) does not relieve the pain of circumcision. It may have limited value afterwards, but is rarely needed. It is best to avoid giving infants any medications they do not need since side effects or sensitization may occur.

✡

Chapter Seven

WHAT IS THE ULTIMATE FATE OF THE FORESKIN?

"Ashes to ashes, dust to dust."

"I am only dust and ashes."

—*Bereshit* 18:27

All parts of the body are supposed to be returned to the earth, and therefore the foreskin should be buried. There is a Conservative protocol for amputated limbs saying, that if possible, they are to be buried with the body. If they are needed for laboratory examinations, they should be buried later. Only under special circumstances when they cannot be buried may they be incinerated.

Sephardic Jews have a wonderful *minhag* or custom of burying the foreskin under a newly planted tree, praying that both the tree and child will grow tall and strong. Today, some modify the custom, planting the foreskin under an already existing tree. I know of no specific prayer to accompany this custom, but some might say a *Shehecheyanu* along with whatever thoughts the parents and family have to share.

Some *mohalim* take the foreskin and bury it themselves. However, I find it a good practice to give this responsibility to the parents. It provides a "teaching moment" and has sparked many a lively conversation. I wrap the foreskin in a foil packet and give it to the parents. Some will bury it right away and let the assembled guests share in the experience. Others will want to wait and bury it later, especially if they decide to plant a tree in honor of their new son. Of course, if the *brit* is not at the parents' home or if they have a special tree in mind, they will bury it later. I always remind them to take the foreskin out of the foil packet.

The planting of a tree, in itself, is a lovely custom associated with birth. In ancient times it was the custom to plant an acacia tree for a girl and a cedar for a boy. When they were to be married, branches from their trees would be cut and used as the poles which hold up the *chuppah*—the wedding canopy.

In the future, some valid medical uses for the foreskin may be developed. Then we will have to seriously consider changing this practice. Until then, it seems best to stay with our time honored traditions.

✡

Chapter Nine

WHEN DO WE HAVE THE BRIT?

CAN WE HAVE A BRIT ON SHABBAT?
CAN WE HAVE A BRIT ON YOM KIPPUR?
CAN WE DO THE BRIT AT NIGHT?

"... throughout the generations, every male among you shall be circumcised at the age of eight days."

Book of Genesis, chapter 17, verse 12

Why eight days? Some speculate that seven days represent the cycle of Creation and that the eighth day signifies the world yet-to-come. As the rite of circumcision evolved others looked to the miracle of Chanukah, which lasted eight days, comparing it with the miracle of birth or equating it with redemption.

My favorite explanation is that when a child is eight days old, he has experienced at least one Shabbat which is also a symbol of the Covenant. How special it is then, when the baby is born on Shabbat, having experienced two Shabbats!

However, many people have been led to believe that we cannot do a Shabbat *brit*. This is because Orthodox *mohalim* will not perform a Shabbat *brit* unless they can walk to, or be put up at, or near, the place where the *brit* is to be performed. They will not violate their Shabbat even though the child's father has the obligation to have the *brit* done on that Sabbath. This is clearly a clash of *mitzvot*—commandments. In such situations the *mohel* often convinces the parents to have the *brit* done on Sunday. Of course if that Sunday and following Monday are *hag*—holy days, such as the first two days of *Pesach*—Passover, the *brit* may not be done until Tuesday.

Most liberal *mohalim* will do a Shabbat *brit* because they will drive to fulfill the *mitvah* of the *brit*. Some *mohalim* certified by the Conservative movement are *shom'rei Shabbat* and will not drive on Shabbat unless it is in their own synagogue.

Actually the *brit* must be done on any holy day, including Yom Kippur. It is tradition to do a Yom Kippur *brit* in the synagogue during the service.

Some look for a medical reason for the eighth-day tradition, and we have one. The baby's clotting factors—blood components that stop bleeding— peak around the eighth day offering protection from bleeding. It is hard to believe this was known at the time of Abraham, although one could argue that God is all-knowing and took this into consideration when choosing the eighth day.

One father offered another contemporary reason. He suggested it had to do with grandparents and family being able to purchase airline tickets with seven days advance notice, thereby saving money. We may never know, but it is said that God works in strange ways.

In determining what is the eighth day, the first day of life is counted as the first day, even if birth occurs minutes before sundown. If the child is born during daylight hours the *brit* will be on the same day of the next week. If the child is born after sundown, it will be the next day, a week later. For example, if a child is born on Monday before sundown, the *brit* is performed on the next Monday. If the child is born on Monday night after sundown, the *brit* is on the following Tuesday. Many follow the tradition of having an early morning *brit* so they may "rush to perform the *mitzvah*." This also allows guests to attend before work, besides assuring there will be sunlight.

The real dilemma occurs when a son is born during twilight, the time between sunset and full night. The question is which part of twilight belongs to one day and which part to the next? The issue is further clouded by published Shabbat candle lighting times which suggest the "official" end of the day. If the day ends at darkness, how is darkness defined? Some say darkness occurs when three stars are visible—but what if it is cloudy or raining?

We must always err away from the seventh day. A *brit* done on the ninth day is considered more "kosher" than one done on the seventh day. We have to consider the word "day" in the *Book of Genesis*, verse 17. It has been interpreted by our sages to mean daylight hours only. The *brit* is not to be performed at night. Otherwise, we could do the *brit* after sundown of the seventh day.

Be careful about scheduling a *brit* close to sundown. Check to make sure the *mohel* is not habitually late or over-booked which might cause arrival after sundown. This is to be prevented if at all possible. Find a *mohel* who is less busy or willing to assure your child's *brit* will be on the correct day—the eighth day.

It is actually required to postpone the *brit* if the baby is not healthy enough to have a circumcision. Then it may be scheduled whenever he is healthy enough for the circumcision to be performed. However, once the eighth day has passed, it may not be done on a Shabbat or holy day.

✡

Chapter Ten
WHAT DO WE DO WITH TWINS ?

Twins present an interesting challenge. They must be healthy enough to circumcise and this may require waiting beyond the eighth day. Most doctors agree that a child should weigh over five pounds and have no other medical problems. If only one twin is healthy on the eighth day, regardless of his brother's condition, his *brit* is to be performed. Parents probably will not like the idea of splitting up the ceremonies, but one compromise would be to do the circumcision for the healthy child on the eighth day with the appropriate blessings, perhaps only including the immediate family, and celebrate the twins' naming together when the second son is healthy enough to circumcise.

There is probably no other situation that requires flexibility on the part of the *mohel* as much as twins. On occasion, if the baby is eight days old or older, *britot* are done in the hospital NICU just before they are sent home. Most hospitals have some type of visitors' room and will make it available. Some Jewish hospitals still have their special *brit* room, created in the time when mothers could stay until the eighth day.

At home, if both children are small and frail, it is not uncommon to circumcise them privately and only bring them out for the naming. One or both of the twins may still require a monitor. Sometimes, a smaller twin or one wearing a monitor is circumcised privately, and the stronger one in public, and then both of them are named together. Of course, if they are both in good health, there is no reason not to perform the entire service as is usually done.

It may be hard to believe, but the question of how to say the blessings for twins has been argued since before the 13th century. It was held that one must not use two sets of blessings if only one was necessary since, ". . . one must guard against committing the sin of pronouncing a blessing unnecessarily." During the mid sixteenth century, discussions in the *Shulchan Aruch*—the Code of Jewish Law—cited established customs in Egypt, where separate blessings were said for each twin, as well as the Ashkenazi custom of combining the blessings. In general, it is our inclination to follow Ashkenazi customs.

Traditions have evolved regarding twins, officially in the *Reform Responsa Dealing With Brit Milah and Related Material* as well as through the practices of both Reform and Conservative rabbis and *mohalim*. Each child is entitled to the benedictions which precede and follow the circumcision as well as the *mishabayrach*—a blessing to be recited for the welfare of the child. When naming the boys it is appropriate to name each of them separately. Prayers which may be said together include: *Baruchim habaim*—blessed are they who enter, *Shehecheyanu*—if said, blessings over wine and bread and the *Birkat Kohanim*—priestly blessings.

Twins present an opportunity to honor many people. Usually there is a separate *sandak, kvater* and *kvaterrin* for each child. However, on occasion, parents choose to have the same *kvater* and *kvatterin* bring each child to either one or two *sandakim*.

Jacob Mollin of Mainz, who lived during the 14th century, even described having two *mohalim*.

When there is a twin son and daughter, many *mohalim* and rabbis combine the *brit* with the girl baby's naming. After circumcising and naming the boy, the girl is named and then they are blessed together.

During the past four decades, many girl naming ceremonies — *Brit Banot, Brit Bat* or *Simchat Bat*—have evolved which may be incorporated into the service.* One custom involves washing the girl's feet because Sarah and Abraham washed the feet of strangers. Candle lighting is often associated with naming girls.

Traditionally, girls are supposed to be named in temple the first time the Torah is read after their birth. The father is given an *aliyah*—the honor of reading the blessing before and after the Torah reading—and his daughter is named. Many parents now opt to name their daughter at home instead. However, there is no prohibition against naming her at home as well as at the temple or synagogue.

Some parents have the naming on the eighth day to parallel *Brit milah.* Because the new moon is associated with women and menstruation, others will choose the first *Rosh Chodesh*—the first day of a new month. However, most parents pick a time when it is most convenient, considering factors like the mother or child's health, when out of town relatives can attend, or just whenever it seems like a good time to have a party.

✡

* Although the topic of girl naming ceremonies is important, it is not the subject of this book. I recommend Anita Diamant's *The New Jewish Baby Book* for more extensive coverage of this subject.

Chapter Eleven

WHO IS HONORED AT A BRIT ?

WHAT ARE THE BASIC HONORS TO BE GIVEN?
DO WE NEED GODPARENTS AT A BRIT?
DO THE "KVATTER" AND "KVATTERIN" HAVE TO BE JEWISH?
DO THE "KVATTER" AND "KVATTERIN" HAVE TO BE MARRIED?

The *Sandak*

The highest honor at a *brit* is given to the *sandak*. The root of this Hebrew word comes from the Greek *sundikos or sunteknos,* which means advocate or helper. This is the person who holds the baby during the circumcision.

Traditionally, he sits on a tall chair like a bar stool, on a table, or in a chair, propped up on pillows. The *sandak* holds the baby on a pillow on his lap. He sits higher because he is supposed to attain the importance of the *Kohen godol*—high priest—his lap becoming an altar.

I say 'he' because in traditional context, this person must be a man. However, liberal Jews will grant this honor to a woman. I have performed a *brit* where a grandmother was the only living grandparent, and although the honor does not have to go to a grandparent, the parents felt she was deserving of this honor. Among Sephardic Jews this honor is always given to the paternal grandfather.

When there are two grandfathers I often suggest two different ways to share this honor:

1. The grandfathers may sit together, side by side, with a pillow across both of their laps, thus sharing the honor.

2. One grandparent can be the "sitting *sandak*" *and* the other the "standing *sandak*" or *sandak sheni*. He or she may also be called the *omed liverachot*—the one who holds the baby during the naming. It is appropriate to grant this honor to a grandparent if the baby is being named after one of his or her relatives.

Tradition states that if a person has been the *sandak* for two children in a family, that he not have that honor again. If there have been two successful *britot*, it is best not to "push one's luck." Sometimes superstition is the driving force in what becomes tradition. Practically, it also spreads the honors to other members of the family.

The *kvatter* and *kvatterin*

In the strictest sense, Judaism does not recognize godparents and yet in many publications on *Brit milah* these roles are attributed to the *kvatter* and *kvatterin*—the man and woman trusted with carrying the baby into the room.

From the secular standpoint, godparents are the couple who have responsibility for the child if the parents become disabled or die. Another tradition says that a godparent sponsors a child as at a baptism or promises to be responsible for its religious upbringing (Webster's New World Dictionary). From this definition we might assume that this couple would be responsible for the child's Jewish education if the parents were not available. This confusion explains why *kvatter/kvatterin* and god parents are so often interchanged.

The fact that the words *kvatter* and *kvatterin* are Yiddish suggests that these roles are only five to six hundred years old, being coined in Central Europe at that time. These may very well be roles adopted from Christian baptism. Contrast these words with the *sandak* which comes from the Greek *sundikos* or *sunteknos*, advocate, helper or companion. The Greeks conquered Israel in 333 B.C.E., and many Hebrew words evolved from the Greek around that time. It is possible that the custom of having a *sandak* is over two thousand years old.

Kvatterin is the feminine form of *kvater* which some say is a contraction of *gottvater*—godfather. If this is the case, then godmother would most likely be *gottmuter* and the Yiddish equivalent might be *gmuter*. Others contend the root of this word equates to "intimate friend."

The most plausible explanation is that *kvater* is a contraction of the Hebrew word, *kavod,* which means honor, and the Yiddish word for door which is *tur.* Thus we have "the honor at the door."

The basic word would be *kvatter* which is masculine and the feminine form of the word would be the *kvatterin.* This makes sense since at a *Brit milah* the *kvatterin* takes the baby from the mother and brings the baby—through the door—into the room and hands it to the *kvatter* who places the baby on the chair of Elijah before the baby is given to the *sandak.*

Whatever the meaning, these roles are usually assigned to very special people in the lives of the parents and baby. It is not unusual for these people to be the very same people who might be given the status of legal guardians in the absence of the parents.

Theoretically, anyone may be given these roles, but it is often given to the child's aunts and uncles. At one *brit* I performed, the parents had seven brothers and sisters and did not want to hurt any feelings. They all participated, "bucket brigading" the baby. Some would argue that this honor should not be diluted, but a better idea is to involve as many people as possible.

It is frequently asked if the *kvatter* and *kvatterin* have to be Jewish. The literature confirms that the *sandak* must be Jewish, but opinions have been written suggesting that the *kvatter* and *kvatterin* do not have to be Jewish. One would certainly think that it would be preferable for them to be Jews, since the role of assuring a Jewish education might be theirs at some future time.

The *kvatter* and *kvatterin* do not have to be married, but there is one custom which has evolved around these roles: If the parents have married friends or relatives who are trying to have a baby and have been unsuccessful, and if they are given this role, it will supposedly enhance their fertility.

I mentioned this to parents who gave this honor to a couple whom I had known for years. Months later I ran into their mother in a supermarket parking lot and she loudly proclaimed that I was a genius. Her daughter was pregnant! I don't know if that gives me genius status, but at least I knew the tradition. When it works, I like to take credit and when it doesn't, I usually say that it is just an "old wives" tale. They had a boy and I had the honor of performing his *brit*.

Other honors

Lighting of candles creates an opportunity to honor more people, particularly grandmothers and great grandmothers. Lighting candles is not obligatory and may not be done on Shabbat. On Shabbat, placing flowers on the table is an appropriate substitute.

Another honor may be given to the person who holds the cup of wine and places wine on the baby's lips. This is often given to a great-grandparent who may be too shaky or weak to actually hold the baby.

There are no other required honors. However, special people can be recognized with other roles. At the end of the service the *hamotzi*—blessing over bread—can be designated prior to eating the meal or refreshments. The blessing over wine is the first part of the traditional naming service and therefore usually is said by the one who is leading this part of the service. In a Reform service this blessing is said after the naming and someone else may be designated to lead it.

Once the child is named, I recommend the family say some words about the person or people for whom the baby is named.

The parents usually participate in blessing the child with the *birkat Kohanim*—the priestly blessing. However, if a family member or friend is a *Kohen,* it is appropriate for him to recite this blessing.

I encourage the parents to add meaningful readings, poems or blessings to the service. Once again this provides an opportunity to honor another person.

Sometimes great-grandparents are unable to participate. Just bringing the baby to them for a kiss is a great honor for them.

A good rule of thumb at a *brit* is that as long as no *halachah*—Jewish Law—is broken, do whatever you can to avoid hurt feelings and to create good memories.

✡

Chapter Thirteen

IS A MINYAN REQUIRED AT A BRIT?

As well as being a frequently asked question, this is a true-false question on the test given to physicians and mid-wives who are to become *mohalim* or *mohalot*. The question asks if this statement is correct:

In traditional Jewish practice, it is preferable to perform circumcision in the presence of a *minyan*—ten Jewish male adults?

The correct answer is "true." The key word in the question is "preferable." Lack of a *minyan* does not negate the validity of the *brit*. A brit may be performed without a *minyan*. Performing the *mitzvah*—commandment—of *Brit milah* takes precedence, superseding the requirement for a *minyan*, just as it overrides the *mitzvot* of Sabbath, Holy Days and festivals.

Orthodox Jews only include men in a *minyan*. Reform, Reconstructionist, and most Conservative Jews include women in a *minyan*.

Consider this question from another perspective. Since a *brit* is a public act of identity, it would be proper for some of the public to be present. A *brit* is the parents' way of introducing their son to the community and declaring that they want him included in our Covenant with God. The presence of a *minyan* at a *Brit milah* assures that this public act of Jewish identity has been performed in the presence of friends, family and the

Jewish community. It can only add to the authority of this ceremony.

However, on one occasion, a couple contacted me shortly after having moved to Los Angeles. Although the mother delivered earlier than expected, she had a healthy baby, so the *brit* could be done on the eighth day. They had no friends or family in Los Angeles. I brought Nancy, my wife, with me, picked up my mother-in-law, who lived nearby, and brought them to the *brit*. Although we didn't have a *minyan*, the parents were thrilled to see that someone in the community cared enough to let them know they were not alone and would welcome their new child to their new community.

This *brit* was as valid as any other *brit*.

✡

Chapter Eight

WHAT ARE THE DIFFERENCES BETWEEN REFORM, CONSERVATIVE AND ORTHODOX BRITOT?

The *Rabbi's Manual* lists a standard service for *Brit milah*. There are differences within each branch of Judaism, but certain basic blessings are common to all of them. Those assembled welcome the child as he enters the room by saying:

Baruch haba—blessed is he who enters.

The child is brought in by the *kvatterin* and *kvatter*, placing him on Elijah's chair saying:

Ze hakisay shel Eliyahu zachur latov—This is the chair of Elijah who is remembered for the good.

The child is placed on the lap of the *sandak* or on a table next to him and some statement is made in reference to the *Book of Genesis*, chapter 17. Then the father says:

Hineni muchan um'zuman lekayaim mitzvat asay shetzivanu haboray yitbarach, lamul et-b'ni, kakatuv b'Torah: uven-sh'monat yamim yimol lachem kol-zachar l'dorotaychem—I am ready to fulfill the *mitzvah* of circumcision, as the Creator commanded us in the Torah: Throughout your generations every male among you shall be circumcised when he is eight days old.

The father then delegates this duty to the *mohel*.

The mohel performs the circumcision saying:

Baruch atah Adonai elohanu melech haolom, asher kideshanu b'mitzvotav vitzivanu al hamilah—Blessed are You, *Adonai*, our God, Creator of the universe, Who sanctified us with Your commandments and commanded us to circumcise.

The father then says:

Baruch atah Adonoi elohanu melech haolom, asher kideshanu bmitzvotav vitzivanu l'hachniso bivrito shel Avraham avinu—Blessed are You, *Adonai* our God, Creator of the universe Who sanctified us with Your commandments and commanded us to bring our son into the Covenant of Abraham our father.

At this point in the traditional service, those assembled will say:

K'shem shenichnas labrit, keyn yikanas l'Torah, ul'chuppah, ul'maasim tovim—
Just as he has entered the Covenant, so may he attain the blessings of Torah, marriage and a life of good deeds.

I have been at Reform services where this prayer is not said here because it is repeated in the naming, but I always include it. The *Brit milah* is a two-part ceremony of identity. The first part is the circumcision granting physical identity, and this prayer officially ends part one.

The second part of the ceremony is the naming, with accompanying blessings. In this part of the ceremony the child is given his spiritual identity. The naming should always be second because, in traditional Judaism, the child's name, especially his Hebrew name, is not revealed until after his circumcision. Many Orthodox Jews will never utter the child's name publicly until after the *Brit milah*. This practice is not followed by the majority of Jews in the United States.

The traditional naming service begins with the blessing over wine, which sanctifies the child's name. It is followed by the naming. Since no one is supposed to know the name, the *mohel* asks the father to say it at the appropriate part of the blessing. The mohel then completes the naming. When the words *Vaomer lach b'damayich chaye* are repeated, drops of wine from the *kiddish* cup are placed on the baby's lips.

An Orthodox *mohel* rarely translates the naming ceremony into English. Most Conservative rabbis who co-officiate or Conservative *mohalim will* translate it. There is a trend not to use the literal translation, but a shorter, contemporary and meaningful one which is found in newer *Rabbi's Manuals*.

After the naming, the Reform service now includes a *Mishabayrach* for the child—a prayer blessing him with a *refu'ah sh'layma*—speedy recovery. It is equally appropriate to recite a prayer for the recovery of the mother.

At this point the parents are encouraged to prepare some words about the child's name. They may include: for whom he was named, their relationship to the child, a meaningful story about them, and some focus on the attributes this person may have had which they hope their son will inherit. I ask parents to write these thoughts so they can be easily read and preserved for the future. Such knowledge is too easily lost over the years. Most liberal rabbis follow this practice as well.

The birkat Kohanim—priestly benedictions are said by all denominations, and then the ceremony is essentially completed. The traditional song, *Siman Tov*, is often sung:

> *Auspicious signs and good fortune.*
> *May these be unto you and to all Israel.*

It is not uncommon for a rabbi to say some personal words or deliver a *drash*—commentary—before closing. A *seudat mitzvah*—festive meal is supposed to follow the *brit*, and it is appropriate that the *hamotzi*—blessing over bread—be said before concluding. Traditionally, whoever says *hamotzi* first washes his hands with the appropriate blessing. In a Reform ceremony the blessing over the wine is said at this point.

On occasion, a Reform or Conservative rabbi will prepare a written service often written in conjunction with the parents. Every once in a while parents will prepare services on their own. It is a good learning experience. Guests often take home copies of the service especially when they are expecting to become parents or grandparents.

I do not prepare any printed service. I choose to have the guests interact with me through blessings that are common to them, asking and answering questions and explaining why we do what we do.

After such a service non-Jews often approach me and thank me for making the service understandable. Surprisingly, many Jews also express their appreciation for my explanation of the meaning of the *brit*. Far too many Jews tell me they have attended *britot* before and never knew what the service was about.

A story to emphasize this occurred a few years back when a guest approached me before a *brit* and told me this was the third *brit* he was attending in a two week period. This was the only one where he heard a meaningful explanation.

Before the actual circumcision I always explain the *Book of Genesis*, chapter 17. Those who have ever attended a *brit* are asked to raise their hands. Then I inquire if anyone knows the meaning of the word *brit*. Almost all of the hands go down and silence ensues except for a rare voice that will say, "Covenant?" Needless to say, the guest mentioned above lowered his hand and didn't have a clue what the word meant. What a shame! There is no better teaching moment then at a *brit*. Most guests are attentive and eager to understand why they are present.

The concept of *hiddur mitzvah*—beautification of the commandment—will also contribute to differences in *britot*. For example, candle lighting is not mandatory, but often done. It beautifies the service and grants *kavod*—honor—to the lighters. Of course, we may not light candles on the Sabbath or Holy days.

Sephardic Jews will often spread rose petals and use ornamented chairs for Elijah. Families may choose to exhibit pictures of those people for whom the child is named. Many use beautiful *brit* gowns for the baby as well as *kiddish* cups that have been passed down through generations.

One need only to visit the Skirball Cultural Center and Museum in Los Angeles to see beautiful ornaments that were created for *britot* hundreds of years ago. The museum also has a wonderful collection of wimples—swaddling cloths which are later decorated with the baby's name, the parent's name, date of birth and the blessing, *"k'shem shenichnas labrit, keyn yikanas l'Torah, ul'chuppah ul'maasim tovim*—just as he has entered the covenant, so may he attain the blessings of Torah, marriage and a life of good deeds." This is a sixteenth century Ashkenazi custom. The wimples were hung in synagogues as birth records and later used as Torah wrappings at *b'nai mitzvah* and at the *aufruf* before weddings.

In determining the differences between *britot*, it is easy to point out the physical and verbal differences. However, two items which are more difficult to define and are most basic center around who is considered Jewish and the qualifications of the *mohel*.

For the Orthodox and Conservative, if the child is not born to a Jewish mother, but the parents want to raise him as a Jew, the *brit* must be done in the presence of a Jewish court, usually consisting of three rabbis or Jewish witnesses, and for the explicit purpose of conversion. The conversion must be completed later by immersion in a *mikvah*. In all other ways, except for the *mohel's* blessing during the circumcision, the *brit* ceremony itself, can be identical to the one used for a boy born to a Jewish woman. The certificate must stipulate that the circumcision was for purposes of conversion.

Needless to say, *britot* done under the authority of patrilineal descent must be done by Reform *mohalim*.

The Orthodox prefer that a *mohel* not be a doctor. They fear that circumcision of non-Jewish babies or any routine circumcisions performed by him will be mistaken for *britot*, and therefore will diminish the act of *brit* as well as the *mohel*. In his book, *Bris Milah*, Henry C. Romberg, M.D., a Lubavitch *mohel*, had to ask for permission from his chief *Rebbe* before he could become a *mohel*. Another Orthodox *mohel* writes:

> The moment of the *bris* has a great spiritual effect upon the child and therefore Jewish law specifies that one should choose a *mohel* who is noted not only for his technical skills but also for his level of piety.

It is interesting that he chose the word piety, which only recognizes one's level of religious practice. Piety in no way assures what I believe to be an equally if not more important requirement—*kavanah*—the proper religious and spiritual intention and attitude which is required at the time of the observance of a *mitzvah*. No matter how pious a *mohel* is, it does not give him the license to tell inappropriate jokes, advertise in the middle of the service, or berate less observant Jews and other *mohalim*. These practices diminish the service as well as the *mohel* himself. Certainly, they are not acts of piety.

The father has the biblical obligation to circumcise his son. The *mohel* is his *shaliach*—designated agent. The parents must carefully consider who will be this agent. In choosing a more pious *mohel* they may be doing themselves a disservice if he will not respect their level of religious practice. I am not suggesting that they seek the least common denominator, but only that parents choose a *mohel* who will understand and respect their approach to Judaism. I am also charging *mohalim* to understand the people they serve and to elevate their level of knowledge and *kavanah* so they can bring love, respect and dignity to this most important commandment.   ✿

Chapter Fourteen

WHAT KIND OF FOOD DO WE SERVE AT A BRIT ?

Food is supposed to be served after a *Brit milah*. The service ends with a *seudat mitzvah*—a festive meal in honor of fulfilling the commandment of the *brit*. The time of day will determine what is appropriate to serve. If the *brit* is held at a meal time, it is only logical for the guests to expect a meal. If the parents are concerned about finances, they might consider having it at an off-hour when only a snack would be in order.

In the Orthodox community it is not unusual to have an elaborate, even sit-down meal. All of the appropriate blessings will be said before and after eating. While some Conservative families will do the same, most will have some type of a buffet. The deli platter has become the standard.

When asked, I urge the family to serve either dairy and/or fish meals. There may be family or guests present, including the *mohel* or rabbi, who cannot or will not mix milk with meat or eat non-kosher meat.

I have been at *britot* where separate tables have been prepared with kosher food for observant guests. Perhaps that is better than nothing at all, but sticking with dairy and/or fish seems easier to me as well as showing concern for all the guests.

Since the guests are going to eat after the service, I remind the family to have a *challah*. Many follow the custom that the *challah* to weigh as much as the baby. An eight pound *challah* is almost three feet long. Traditionally, the *hamotzi*—blessing over bread—is said after washing hands with the appropriate blessing in preparation for the festive meal.

In saying the blessing over the wine, some suggest using a white Concord grape wine to spare the tablecloth. However, most agree that the more traditional ceremonial wine is a sweet red Concord grape. If you want your guests to participate in the blessing over the wine together and you are worried about spilling wine on your light carpet, consider using taller paper cups instead of the one ounce plastic cup typically used. Also, keep in mind that pouring wine for everyone is an option.

Finally, there are a number of fast days, the best known one being *Yom Kippur*. In this case, it is not unusual to do the *Brit milah* in the synagogue. The baby will still be given wine and a recovering mother is allowed to eat for health purposes. An appropriate way for everyone to celebrate later would be with a break-the-fast meal.

Passover requires special food considerations. It is appropriate that they also be maintained at the *brit*.

Tisha b'Av is a lesser known fast day. Some do a "half-fast" and perform the *brit* later in the day, celebrating with a late lunch or early dinner. Another way is to have the *brit* just before sundown and then eat after sundown. Some other fast days include the *Fast of Gedalia*, the *Fast of Esther*, the *10th of Tevet,* and the *17th day of Tammuz*. These are even less well known fast days, and the same suggestions mentioned above with regard to *Tisha b'Av* apply to these fasts as well.

✡

Chapter Fifteen
WHAT IS WORN AT A BRIT ?

The Baby

The baby may wear essentially anything as long as there are no pant legs. Most wear some type of a gown which ties or has elastic at the bottom, but even a plain shirt is acceptable. On occasion, a friend or relative will buy an expensive, elaborate two-or-three-piece outfit with legs. The parents, not wanting to hurt any feelings, insist on clothing the baby in it, even if it is inappropriate. *Mohalim* can work with almost anything, but keep in mind that the most important thing is to have easy access to the child's genital area.

Most *mohalim* have no preference as to what type of diaper is worn but disposable diapers are quicker and a little easier to manage.

I have performed *britot* where the child is the fifth generation to wear the gown including the baby's father and grandfather, who was the *sandak*. That can create a very emotional moment.

Some gowns are made with beautifully hand-crafted lace with separate vests and hats, similar to baptismal gowns. These gowns are not foreign to Judaism, having been used for hundreds of years. Invariably, wine will spill on the gown, but it always washes off. If wine does spill on the gown, I usually tell the parents the gown is not official until it has wine on it. By the way, Dior makes a very nice line of gowns that is relatively inexpensive and fortunately, they say "Baby Dior" instead of "Christian Dior."

After the circumcision, before the naming, many parents will wrap the baby in a receiving blanket. Most babies are comforted by swaddling. In an earlier chapter, I discussed wimples which are usually made from the cloth in which the baby is swaddled. A thirty inch square of cloth may be cut up later on and fashioned into a banner which will be decorated as a wimple.

Many people buy a *kippah*—skullcap—and/or a *tallit*—prayer shawl—for the baby. The wearing of these items by an infant is not required by Jewish law. Some skullcaps come with a strap which is tied under the baby's chin and others are virtually impossible to keep on the baby unless you use doubled-up tape. If there is a special family *tallit* I have often suggested wrapping the baby in it when he is brought in or for the naming.

Family and Guests

This question is not asked too often, but when it is, I love to answer it by saying, "Whatever you would wear to temple or synagogue." Being a bit old fashioned, this usually means a suit or jacket. However, in my life time, tremendous changes in what men will wear to temple have occurred. In many ways it parallels what is worn to the symphony or theater. After arguing with my children about wearing tennis shoes to a friend's *bar mitzvah*. I spoke to my rabbi . His philosophy was, " I don't care what they wear as long as they attend."

So now I have to be content when a father doesn't wear

shorts, jeans or cutoffs and a tank top or t-shirt. Actually, nothing is wrong with a nice shirt and slacks. Women almost always seem to dress appropriately.

Contrast this with an Orthodox *brit* in Israel or anywhere else in the world. Men will be clothed in their black suits and fedoras and *kippot* and women will wear dresses and often hats. However, if you go out to the kibbutzim or to other "secular" Israeli *britot*, men will wear slacks and open necked shirts.

Often, the time of the *brit* determines what the guests wear. During the week, men or women coming from, or going to work, will attend in what they wear to work. In those cases, it is not unusual for the father to wear a tie and a jacket. Mothers usually wear whatever fits and looks nice. On the weekends, dress tends to be more casual. Dress also seems to vary with the geographical location.

Most men participating in the ceremony will wear a *kippah*. Hosts usually provide *kippot* for their guests. I always carry a dozen with me. Grandparents always seem to have an extensive collection of *kippot*, and parents often have left over *kippot* from the wedding.

The father and *sandak* may wear a *tallit*, and a good many do.

✡

Chapter Seventeen
DO WE NEED A RABBI
AT THE BRIT ?

Until 1984 most *mohalim* were either rabbis or cantors. I visited one small town in the Soviet Union where the local kosher meat slaughterer had been the *mohel*. If no *mohel* was available, it was not unusual for the family's rabbi to say the blessings with a local Jewish doctor performing the circumcision. In that situation, obviously the rabbi was necessary.

In 1984 the Reform movement started training physicians, nurses and certified nurse midwives to become certified *mohalim* and *mohalot*. Subsequently, the Conservative movement began training physician-*mohalim* and to date, the two movements have certified over three hundred *mohalim* and *mohalot*. Applicants must show proof of expertise in circumcision as well as religious affiliation before they are taught the appropriate blessings and background materials to qualify as a *mohel*.

Most *britot* are performed without the presence of a rabbi. However, I heartily recommend and endorse a rabbi being in attendance, always looking forward to what the rabbi has to say and invariably learning something new.

Rabbis are usually invited if the celebrating family is affiliated with a synagogue, or if they have had a previous relationship with the rabbi, such as having officiated at the marriage ceremony of the couple. Sometimes the grandparents are affiliated and request their rabbi to attend. Occasionally a cantor is invited, sometimes with, and other times without a rabbi.

When it comes to life cycle events, rabbinical styles vary tremendously. Some are "hands on" rabbis who somehow juggle an amazingly busy schedule to attend every *brit*. Some rarely come. I know a few rabbis who almost always bring their cantors with them. When performing *britot* for rabbis or temple officials, as many as five rabbis were in attendance. It was a challenge to find some way for all of them to participate.

Since the *Brit milah* service easily divides into the circumcision and the baby naming, the responsibilities of the *mohel* and *rabbi* seem obvious. Once in a while I will ask the rabbi, jokingly, if he or she would care to trade jobs. For some reason, they always decline.

On occasion a rabbi wants to be a guest rather than an official, but even in these cases they will usually say a few words or the priestly blessings. However, at one *brit*, a rabbi wanted to do everything except the circumcision and the one blessing that accompanies it. When a situation like that occurs, the best thing a *mohel* can do is step aside and let the rabbi do whatever he or she wants.

The relationship between the *mohel* and the family is fleeting (unless they have more boys), while hopefully the rabbi and the family, as well as the rabbi and the *mohel*, will have a long relationship.

✡

Chapter Eighteen

HOW CAN THE BRIT
BE MADE MORE EGALITARIAN?

During the traditional morning blessing-*birkot hashachar*—a man thanks God that he is not a woman. This prayer has been removed from the Conservative and Reform service. There were times in our history, particularly during the middle ages, when women were not even permitted to attend a *Brit milah*. In his before mentioned book *Bris Milah*, Henry C. Romberg, M.D., a Lubavitcher *mohel*, lists seven participants in the ceremony, and states that six out of the seven must be males. The one woman is the *kvatterin*. For him, this is a fact not open to interpretation or change. The traditional *Brit milah* ceremony is typical of what we find throughout Orthodox Jewry in that it is male oriented and male dominated.

Contrast that with the modern, liberal movements of Judaism that now ordain women rabbis and cantors. Reform Judaism even certifies women ritual circumcisers—*mohalot* and there are no prohibitions in the Conservative movement against a woman being a *mohelet*. There is biblical precedent for a woman performing a *brit*. In the *Book of Exodus* 4:25-26, Tziporrah, the wife of Moses, circumcises her son.

I have co-officiated at many *britot* with both female rabbis and female cantors and frequently recommend a local *mohelet* when I am not available.

Obviously, if the officials at these ceremonies may be women, other changes are sure to follow—and they have. Over the past few decades, gender-sensitive translations of the liturgy have been created. Women now take part in previously 'men only' roles. New roles are being created for women, and mothers are taking a central part in the *brit*.

How do we make the liturgy gender sensitive? One way is to recognize that we could not have had fore-fathers without fore-mothers. So instead of saying, "God of our fathers," some now say, "God of our fathers and mothers," or "God of our ancestors." We honor not only Abraham, Isaac and Jacob, but also Sarah, Rebecca, Rachel and Leah. We even account for the mother when we name the baby. The baby is now named as the son of the father and mother.

Attempts are now being made to refer to God with gender-neutral language. Newer liturgies frequently depict God as the 'Eternal' or 'Creator' instead as 'Lord', 'Ruler' or 'He'.

Recognizing that there are now gay, lesbian, and single parents, in one prayer book, the word *chuppah*—marriage canopy—is interpreted to signify a "significant and meaningful family relationship."

As said before, the lighting of candles is not obligatory at a *brit* but can be significant at two levels; beautifying the service and honoring the grandmothers. For the most part, great-grandmothers and grandmothers are ignored in the traditional ceremony, and this is a good way to honor them. Traditionally, women are our candle lighters. If the *brit* occurs on the Sabbath or a Holy day, candles may not be lit. When that happens, grandmothers may carry in some flowers and place them on the table.

Frequently, after the circumcision, before the naming, I will pass the baby 'through the generations,' from great grandparents to grandparents to the parents.

Classically, the mother would not even attend the *brit*. She would be off in another room with the women or in the doorway looking away. Now the mothers, grandmothers and women guests are 'up front and personal.' They want to see what is going on and participate in the blessings and be supportive to the family. They are a welcome addition. It is common for the mother to participate in saying some significant words about the person for whom the baby was named.

Over the years I have seen maybe seven or eight men faint at the service but only one woman. She was a young woman standing in the back of the room.

I was told that she had fainted at another *brit* a few weeks before. Perhaps she thought that it was like falling off when riding a horse. She had to try again as soon as possible.

✡

Chapter Nineteen
HOW DO WE CHOOSE A MOHEL?

"Why should I choose you as a *mohel?*" That question has only been asked of me once in all of my years as a *mohel*. It had such an impact, that I couldn't answer it immediately. Eventually I did, and was chosen to perform the *brit*. The discussion in this chapter is a result of the thought process that ensued and how I have tried to mold my practice as a *mohel*. I will share some of my most personal thoughts about this subject and must admit there will be some bias. However, I hold anyone who is entrusted with the job of being a *mohel* to both the highest medical and religious standards.

Most people choose a *mohel* as the result of a recommendation from either a friend, religious professional or their doctor or a nurse. It is not unusual for *mohalim* to advertise in local Jewish publications and some *mohalim* even have Web sites. I have been able to develop a substantial practice by word-of-mouth and with recommendations from rabbis, temples, synagogues, doctors and medical personnel. When we trained as *mohalim/ot,* we were told that we represented the Jewish community and that our decorum should always be in good taste. Too often advertising crosses that line.

Some families will call me during the pregnancy and establish a relationship as they "shop" for a *mohel*. Others call for the first time right after the baby is born and frantically try to make an informed decision. It is preferable to have established some kind of a relationship before the delivery. This allows the family to prepare for the *brit* under more relaxed circumstances. Since I always schedule *britot* on a "first come-first served" basis, there is never any guarantee they will get the time they want. They know to call as soon as possible and they already know what is needed for the *brit*. If they don't use my services, at least they now know how to get ready for the *brit*.

It is not unusual for a temple or synagogue to list two or three recommendations. Often the father, after the birth, will frantically call all of them, booking the first one that calls back. That is not the best reason to choose a *mohel*.

Another situation that often leads to desperation is if the family has locked themselves into a specific time. Then they are at the mercy of whoever is available. I know people who booked a hotel, temple or restaurant before they called the *mohel*. It seems that their priorities need some adjustment. But then again, I'm a *mohel*, so how else would I see it?

Now, if all *mohalim* had equal skills, I wouldn't be so concerned. If I had to choose a *mohel* for my own family, how would I come to a decision? First and foremost, the *mohel* or *mohelet* would have to perform a good circumcision. In listing the *mohalim/ot* I know, I would not necessarily always choose a doctor-*mohel* or nurse-midwife-*mohel* before a rabbi-*mohel*. It would depend on their experience and reputation, which is determined by talking to other parents, doctors and/or rabbi(s).

As you know, I prefer the Gomco clamp. If there were no anatomical contraindications, I could allow someone who uses a Mogen clamp, but it would not be my first choice.

Other factors would have to come into play. I, personally, would never use a *mohel* who uses a Mogen <u>shield</u> for two reasons: I don't think they are as good as clamps, and anyone who uses one would obviously be an ultra-Orthodox *mohel*.

The reason I could never use an Orthodox *mohel* has to do with the fact that within certain limits, I think the level of religious practice and beliefs of the *mohel* should be compatible with the family's practices and beliefs. For example, if the mother had a Reform, Reconstructionist or Conservative conversion, any Orthodox *mohel* would consider neither the mother nor child to be Jewish. They might agree to do the *brit* but only if they could bring three rabbis with them as witnesses to constitute a *beit din* —rabbinical court—as a first step to the child "converting" to Judaism. The Orthodox are *mitzvah* driven. Their main concern is that the commandments are performed according to their rules. In doing so, they deny the authority of other denominations.

Why do people will put up with this behavior, denying their own level of practice? It is equally puzzling that there are non-Orthodox rabbis who continue to recommend these *mohalim*, especially when they know the mother is a convert.

It used to bother me when someone would book a *brit* with me and cancel it as late as the night before because one Orthodox member of the family talked the family into changing *mohalim*, and that the second *mohel* would actually agree to do it. Now I just accept it as a fact of life, and whenever there is an inkling that there are any Orthodox family members, I suggest they contact an Orthodox *mohel* in order to maintain family harmony. This should not be a time of strife for the parents. They have enough to deal with and it creates bad feelings - what is known as *sinat chinam*—causeless hatred. This should be avoided at all costs.

That doesn't mean that I think a non-affiliated family should use a non-affiliated *mohel.* In many instances a non-Orthodox family may be very comfortable with an Orthodox *mohel*, particularly if the mother is Jewish by birth. However, particularly with families who are not as observant, I think they would be better off with a *mohel* who will translate Hebrew blessings and explain what is going on and why we do what we do. Therefore, in order of priorities for choosing a *mohel*, second to the ability to perform the circumcision is the *mohel's* level of observance and how it relates to me and my family. There has to be a two-way level of respect.

I am not trying to undermine any good rabbi-*mohel* relationship. There are some Orthodox *mohalim* who cooperate with their non-Orthodox colleagues, and they are to be commended. Rabbi William Lebeau, Vice-Chancellor of the Jewish Theological Seminary of America in New York City, was co-creator of its *Brit Kodesh* program which trains Conservative physicians to be *mohalim*. Rabbi Lebeau told me that their policy is not to train *mohalim* in areas where there are Orthodox *mohalim* who cooperate with Conservative rabbis.

My theoretical selection process now turns from professional to personal considerations. If all things are equal, I must consider the personality of the *mohel*, his or her decorum, level of professionalism and fees. I am a "people person," and I enjoy talking about *Brit milah*. That is why I don't resort to too much printed information or web sites. I believe questions are best answered person-to-person.

For example, in order to choose a name, I could refer someone to a naming dictionary, but my familiarity with names and extracting information about the people for whom the baby is being named can save hours of precious time. In choosing the honorees at the *brit*, some understanding of the family dynamics may save embarrassment. In sizing up the family and their level of religious practice, I can prepare some appropriate thoughts which may enhance the service. So obviously, I would like a *mohel* to treat me the same way that I treat people.

Price would not be the number one consideration for me, but it is for many young struggling couples. My fee has always been at the low end of the scale. If there is any problem, it is whatever they can afford—even if nothing. I have performed *britot* for nothing and even brought the wine and *challah*. I don't believe in someone having to make installment payments either. That is demeaning to the parents.

In all fairness, there have been times when people have misrepresented themselves to be in need. When I arrived at their expensive home, there were fancy cars in the garage and an elaborate, catered spread to be served. It was hard not to feel deceived, but according to Jewish tradition, if someone is in need and is used to a certain level of living, in order for them to maintain their self-respect and dignity, we are obligated to help them maintain that level. It is better to give them the benefit of the doubt.

Professionalism may be hard to define, but people recognize and are influenced by it. I find it amusing that many non-medical *mohalim* wear a white coat or jacket, trying to look like a doctor, while most doctors (including myself) wear a suit or jacket, trying to look more like a rabbi.

Some *mohalim* are notoriously late, and that effects a lot of people, especially if the guests have to go to work or have brought their children. It creates a lot of stress for the parents and the baby. Either these *mohalim* overbook, not allowing enough time, or think it is fashionable to be late, lending an air of being very busy. This is particularly distressing at the end of the day because the *brit* must be done before sundown.

And then there are the *mohalim* who think they are stand-up comedians. Enjoying a good joke as much as anyone, I choose to insert humor at certain times in the service in order to break the tension or make a point, while never forgetting that this is a religious service which demands respect. It is all a matter of balance. Most of those assembled would love to hear some explanation about what is going on rather than a string of one-liners.

The *brit* is a perfect teaching opportunity with a captive audience. Some will not be Jewish. If people can leave with an understanding of what they have seen, they will begin to look at *Brit milah* in an entirely different context than before.

The *mohel* has a unique opportunity and responsibility to help guide new parents through a potentially difficult time with compassion, while maintaining a passion for fulfilling the *mitzvah* of *Brit milah*. Often, the *mohel* is the first religious functionary a couple has encountered since their wedding. The *mohel's* behavior may very well set the tone for the couple's future religious involvement. This is not a task to be taken lightly.

Most *mohalim* with whom I have been acquainted are terrific people. And if you are not happy with your choice, just remember, I had three sons long before I became a *mohel*. I was able to choose three different times. Maybe you will, too.

✡

Chapter Twenty
HOW MUCH SHOULD A MOHEL COST?

Following in the tradition of Abraham, it is incumbent upon the father to circumcise his son. However, most fathers neither have the expertise nor the stomach to do so. That is why the father is allowed to appoint a *shaliach*—agent—to perform the circumcision on his behalf. Traditionally, if the father could not afford to pay a *mohel*, it was the obligation of the community to see that the *mitzvah* was performed.

A contemporary example of such a need occurred with Operation Exodus, the Russian immigration to both Israel and the United States. Most Russian Jews were not circumcised, and when they arrived many of us were called on by rabbis or community service organizations to perform the *mitzvah* of circumcision. These services were readily given free of charge.

Traditionally, it has been appropriate to compensate the *mohel* for his work. In 1984, when the first group of physician - *mohalim/ot* was trained, the question of fee was discussed. Basically, it was felt that the fee should be affordable, and different figures were considered. However, it was also recognized that among physicians no one could dictate what someone else should charge. All that could be done was to establish guidelines.

In the greater Los Angeles area, where the first group of non-Orthodox *mohalim* was trained, there was a wide variety in what physicians charged for the same procedure. Finally, it was agreed that the guideline would be the sum of what it would cost to have a circumcision done in the office or hospital plus the charge for an office visit. This seemed fair and was within the range of what local *mohalim* were charging at the time.

When I became a *mohel* in 1984, the average price for a *brit* in Los Angeles was between $190 and $250. In 1998, fees range from $300 to $550. Charges in New York City have always been slightly higher. Don't be afraid to ask beforehand.

One added feature of using a physician-*mohel* is the ability to submit the circumcision part of the charge for insurance reimbursement. If the insurance plan pays for an office or hospital circumcision, it will pay for the circumcision part of the *Brit milah*. Legally, the physician may charge for the circumcision and anesthesia, if given by injection only. Some companies will pay for the sterile tray. Consultations and office visits are not paid for. If the physician tries to pad the bill to increase reimbursement, the insured, as well as he or she, are at risk for fraud.

Most *mohalim/ot* make their services available to everyone and will adjust their fee according to the needs of the family. If someone lives in an area where there is only one *mohel*, this could be a problem if he or she was not affordable and unwilling to adjust the fee. In that case the only other option would be to use a rabbi and a Jewish physician who hopefully would charge less, or be able to provide financial relief through insurance. In most metropolitan areas people now have a choice of *mohalim* and can find one who will be able to accommodate them. If unable to do so, discussing your dilemma with a local rabbi is often beneficial.

When it comes to doctors or *mohalim*, there is no direct correlation between ability and fee. Don't be afraid to discuss and compare fees. More is not necessarily better. ✡

Chaper Twenty-one

HOW DO WE NAME THE OUR BABY?
MAY WE NAME OUR SON AFTER A LIVING PERSON?
MAY WE NAME A MALE AFTER A FEMALE?
IF WE USE A YIDDISH NAME, DO WE ALSO HAVE TO GIVE A HEBREW ONE?
ARE SOME NAMES TO BE AVOIDED?

The moment of the circumcision is certainly the holiest moment of the *Brit milah* service, charged with anticipation, anxiety and finally, relief. However, the most meaningful and significant moment for the family often is when the name is given. As indicated earlier, after the naming, many rabbis and *mohalim* ask the parents to prepare some words about the person or people for whom the baby is being named. Their responses vary from a few brief comments to lengthy prepared speeches which run the gamut of emotion.

Traditionally, the name is not made public until after the circumcision has been performed. In Biblical times the child was named at the time of birth, but in post-Talmudic times the present practice was established. During the naming ceremony it is not unusual for the *mohel* or the rabbi to ask the father to publicly state his son's name for the first time. However, now-a-days we often drive up to the home and see a large wooden stork on the lawn with the child's name and vital statistics written on it or we find a large computerized print out with a "welcome home . . . . " (You fill in the name). So much for keeping the name a secret!

Parents can still maintain some tradition by not publicly displaying the child's Hebrew name. Of course if the child has a Hebrew or biblical name to start with, the element of surprise is gone.

Some people know what they will name their children before they are even conceived while most will decide by the time the baby is born. However, even with nine months to decide on a name, there are still those parents who cannot decide upon a name even up to the time of the *brit*.

Many factors go into choosing a name for a Jewish child. By far, the main reason is to honor a deceased relative. The next most common reason is the parents just liking a name because of the way it sounds. It is often used in conjunction with a name they have to use because of compelling family reasons. That is why we see so many combinations of Jewish and non-Jewish names like Sean David or Collin Jacob. Often the choice will be dictated by the popular names of the day since names do run in cycles. Many questions arise as a name is considered.

1.   May we name a child after a living person? In his commentary to *Sefer Chasidim*, H. J. D. Azuli said, "A man does not call a son by his own name." We rarely see a Jewish "Junior" or "the Third" unless there is a mixed marriage where the father is not Jewish. It is not typical for Jews to name a son after the living father. However, when it comes to naming after a living grandfather, the practice differs: Ashkenazi Jews do not name after a living person, but the Sephardim will name a first son after the living paternal grandfather. Both practices involve different interpretations of how best to ward off the Angel of Death.

Ashkenazi Jews in times past feared that if there was an old man and an infant with the same name, the angel might take the young one by mistake or the older man would die prematurely. A person's name was the absolute identity of his soul, and when the name was given to a child, the soul could not coexist in two bodies at the same time, and so it would have to leave the body of one to enter the other.

However, the Sephardim believed they could trick the angels by confusing them, and in that way the grandfather and the grandchild would both be spared and perhaps the angels would choose someone else with a similar name. (That's not a bad idea if it works unless you're the person with the similar name!) One of the classic examples of such a practice was the famous Jewish poet Judah Halevi who cites his grandson in one of his poems with the words, "How can Judah (the grandfather) ever forget Judah (the grandson)?"

On many occasions I have known couples to ask an aging relative if they may honor him or her with their name, and doing so if he or she consented. After all, in *Sefer Chasidim* it is said, "Superstitions can affect only those who believe in them."

Superstitions aside, modern Jews often make this decision simply on the basis of the family member they would like to honor. This also produces a sense of family continuity. Ashkenazi Jews get around the problem of possibly offending a living relative whose name they did not choose by restricting the names they choose to deceased relatives. However, one still has to appease the living relatives of the other possible people who were not chosen. Sephardic Jews circumvent the problem completely, by having a prescribed order of naming: the paternal grandfather for the first son, the maternal grandfather for the second, the paternal great-grandfather for the third son, etc.

2.   May we name a boy after a female? Here are some of the factors that prompted this question. Transmigration of the soul—the belief that the souls of the departed re-enter this world and are reborn—was popular by the late seventeenth century. It was considered vital to give the name of an ancestor to a child so that the soul could "stay in the family." However, giving the name of a man to a woman, or vice versa, was another thing. As said before, traditional male Jews recite a benediction daily thanking God for not having made him a woman. If a man's soul was reborn in a woman, he would have to live his new life as a woman.

Contemporary practices ignore such superstitions. There are some names which may be used with either sex. *Simchah* is such an example. It is not uncommon for a male child to be named after a female and the corollary—in the opposite direction—is just as true. In such cases, parents choose a name that is gender-appropriate for the child but which captures the meaning or repeats the first letter of the person after whom the child is named. However, when boy and girl twins are born, the parents usually will name along gender lines.

3.   If the child has a Yiddish name, does he need a Hebrew one as well? Parents will rarely choose a Yiddish name unless it is after a deceased relative. Grandpa *Herschel* may not have had an English name, and the parents may have decided to call their son Harold or Harrison or to give him a name that had nothing to do with the letter H. *Herschel* is a Yiddish variant of *Hersch* which means a deer, a sign of strength and grace. The Hebrew equivalent is *Tzvi*, and it is not unusual to have someone called *Tzvi Hersch* which obviously means "deer deer." This will occur when someone insists the child have a Hebrew name. *Dov Beryl* "bear bear" is another common union of Hebrew and Yiddish.

It has been written that Jews were redeemed from Egpyt for several reasons, among them being: we kept our Jewish names and thus our identity and we did not stop circumcising. Some authorities have objected to the use of non-Hebrew names, and this may have prompted combining Hebrew and Yiddish names. Names are used when someone is called to the Torah and it was felt that heavenly authorities would find it easier to recognize a Hebrew name. However, from Talmudic times to the present, non-Hebrew names have been used, and they most likely will continue to be used through the on-coming generations.

4. Are there some names that should not be used ? At one time it was prohibited to use any Biblical name prior to Abraham. That practice has certainly fallen by the wayside. We all know of an Adam or Noah. There are almost 2,800 names in our Bible that are never used more than once.

It is difficult to believe any Jew would name their son *Haman* (probably from the Persian "to rage or to be turbulent"). However, Hamen or Hyman is a common last name and is derived from the Anglo-Saxon "one who lives in a high place, or on a mountaintop." Because of Hitler, some will not call a son Adolph even if a relative had that name. They will usually use some other name starting with the letter A.

There are many popular names we would probably avoid if we only went by what they mean. Consider *Devorah* or Deborah which means a "swarm of bees." Fortunately, the Biblical Deborahs—Rebecca's nurse in *Genesis* 35:8 and the prophetess-judge wife of *Lapidot* in *Judges* 4:5—were admirable characters and the meaning "to speak kind words" is a better representation of this name. Would you name a daughter "sea of bitterness?" And yet that is one of the meanings of the name of a true biblical heroine, Miriam, the sister of Moses. If someone I loved had that name I would rather translate her name from the Chaldaic, meaning "mistress of the sea."

You might want to stay away from *Korach* for a son. He was the Levite who led a rebellion against the leadership of Moses and Aaron, and failed when the earth opened and swallowed him along with 250 rebels. Anyway, *Korach* means "bald." How many of you would choose *Achlav, Cheilav, Eval* or *Machlon* knowing these names mean "fat?" A very popular Hebrew name is *Gidon* which means either "maimed" or a "mighty warrior."

One will not find too many, if any, Jewish Christophers. However, I once performed a circumcision for conversion on a seventeen month old child named Christopher who was adopted from Bulgaria. Needless to say, the parents legally changed his name before the *Bet din* and *mikvah*.

The primary goal in choosing a name was to promote the welfare and future destiny of the child. Our ancestors believed the child would take on the traits of the person who bore that name or the very trait the name meant (for example, *Chanan* means compassion). Naming a child after a "wicked" relative or person was to be avoided in order to prevent transfer of the evil traits from the "wicked" person to the child. In contrast, it was appropriate to name the child after a righteous person.

It was considered bad luck to use the name of a person who was murdered. If parents named a child after another child of theirs who died, it was the practice to combine that name with another one. In Jewish Yemen they even named a child after the father, if he had lost other children, in order to gain his protection.

Perhaps the only rule in naming a baby is to remember that there are no rules. When choosing a name, consider the following:

1. Decide whether you want to name your child after a relative, and if so, which one.

2. If there are direct English translations of the Hebrew name, consider them first. If the parents don't like them, or they have been used before in the family or it is the name of a living relative, consider a variant of the name, such as *Micha* for *Michael*. More than one relative in a family may have the same name. Different relatives may name their child after the same person.

3. Where there is no direct translation, consider using the same first letter. This is particularly difficult with William since there are no Hebrew names beginning with W. Yiddish names beginning with W are pronounced with a V such as Volf, and the only two Hebrew names beginning with V, *Vered* and *Varda* are usually used for girls. In this case many choose a name starting with B for Bill. The letter F also presents problems since there are only Yiddish names beginning with this letter. In this case many use Hebrew names that begin with EF sounds such as *Ephrayim*. The letter J is pronounced as a Y in Hebrew. Therefore Jonah become *Yonah*.

4. If you do not like any name with the same letter, consider using the meaning of the name, especially if it is Yiddish, and find a Hebrew name with the same meaning. For example, Lawrence is from the Latin "laurel" or "crown." A suitable equivalent is *Katriel*—"God is my crown."

5. If there are two English names and the first one is a name chosen because you like it and the second name honors

someone, you have several options:

a. Choose equivalent Hebrew names for both names.

b. Choose a single Hebrew name after only one of the names.

c. Choose completely different Hebrew names which have nothing to do with the English names. As with English names, more than one middle name may be used, but today, common practice is to use only one middle name.

d. Use one Hebrew name from either of the English names and a completely different second Hebrew name which has nothing to do with the other English name and may or may not be honoring someone.

6. Although the most popular reasons for choosing a name are just liking it or naming it after someone, there are other reasons for choosing a name, such as:

a. A holiday or event at the time of birth—*Pesach* or *Simchah* are good examples.

b. A place you visited or like. One couple met in the mountains and their child's second name was Dakota. The Hebrew name was *Harel* or "mountain of God."

c. Names have been chosen after animals (*Dov*—bear, *Tzvi*—deer, *Aryeh*—lion), flowers, plants or trees (*Varda*—rose, *Shoshanah*—lily, *Elan*—oak tree), attributes (*Haskel*—wisdom, *Chanan*—compassion, *Eitan*—strength), patriarchs or matriarchs, kings or queens, heroes, geographic sites in Israel, celebrities and just about any other reason you might consider.

7. The sound of a name, especially in conjunction with another name, might be distasteful. Some names combined with others are lyrical and seem to flow while others sound harsh or guttural. It is all a matter of personal preference.

8. If a boy's name is also used for girls, and you are afraid children will tease him about it, you may want to avoid using it. Most will not follow the logic of the father in the Country Western song sung by Johnnie Cash entitled *A Boy Named Sue*.

9. There are names that take on a different meaning in another language which may cause embarrassment.

10. Try using a naming dictionary. Most synagogues or temples have one or two in their library or book store, and there is a good chance you know someone who owns one. I rely on *The Complete Dictionary of English and Hebrew First Names* by Alfred J. Kolatch (Jonathan David Publishers, Inc., New York, 1984). Other resources include *The Complete Book of Hebrew Baby Names* by Smadar Shir Sido, (Harper and Row, San Francisco, 1989) and *The New Jewish Baby Book* by Anita Diamant, (Jewish Lights Publishing, Woodstock, Vermont, 1994).

11. When all else fails, consult your rabbi or *mohel*. However, in the end, the choice is yours.

✡

Chapter Twenty-two

WHERE CAN WE MAKE A DONATION HONORING THE CHILD?

When one eats and drinks himself, it is his duty to feed the stranger, the orphan, the widow and other poor and unfortunate people, for he who locks the doors to his courtyard and eats and drinks with his wife and family without giving anything to eat and drink to the poor and the bitter in soul—his meal is not a rejoicing in a divine commandment, but a rejoicing in his own stomach.

The Code of Maimonides, 12th Century

It is a Jewish tradition to give a portion of all gifts received to charity. This is not surprising, since the act of *tzedakah*—giving to charity—is an important Jewish principle. During the *Brit milah* we recognize the prophet Elijah who reminds us we are obligated to do *tikkun olam*—repair of the world—through acts of loving kindness and charity. Therefore, it makes sense at the time of bringing our children into the Covenant of Abraham to be mindful of those less fortunate.

It is not uncommon when Jews have a *simchah*, like a wedding or *bar/bat mitzvah*, to consider contributing two to three percent of what was spent on the *simchah* to charity. Since eating is an important part of these events and required at a *Brit milah*, a logical charitable contribution centers around food. MAZON is a charity which helps feed those who are unable to provide for themselves. Also, local food banks are present in most communities. Unfortunately, for reasons of health and cleanliness, leftover food from the *brit* may not be given to shelters, but canned and wrapped foods are gladly welcomed.

I usually suggest that when parents are planning to enjoy their *seudat mitzvah*—festive meal—to take some time to consider also feeding the hungry. One way to involve the community in this project is to have a *tzedakah* box on the table and let the guests know where the proceeds will go.

It is always appropriate to make a donation given in honor of the child. Parents may even consider designating either MAZON, their temple or synagogue, or a favorite charity on the invitation in lieu of gifts. Many parents make a donation in honor of their new child.

When performing *Brit milah* for parents who are affiliated with congregations, I personally make a donation in the name of the child to their temple or synagogue. For those who are unaffiliated, I make contributions to the *Brit milah* program at the Hebrew Union College, the Conversion program and the *mikvah* at the University of Judaism, or MAZON. In doing so, I hope to lead by example.

Chapter Twenty-three

DOES A BRIT MAKE MY SON JEWISH?

WHAT ARE THE DIFFERENCES BETWEEN ORTHODOX, CONSERVATIVE, RECONSTRUCTIONIST AND REFORM CONVERSIONS?

Herman Ginsburg is making his annual winter trip from Chicago to Florida where he will take in the sun, *kibbitz*, play cards with his cronies and, most important, play his beloved game of golf as often as he can. While driving through Georgia he notices a beautiful, lush golf course and nearing the entrance, he reads, "White Bread Country Club - Members Only." Undaunted by the sign he drives into the parking lot, parks his car and goes up to the club pro saying, "Hello, I'm Herman Ginsburg from Chicago and this is my membership card from Ravesloe Country Club. I spotted your beautiful club and would like you to grant me reciprocity so I can play your wonderful course."

Dumbfounded, the pro said, "I'm sorry, but no non-member may play this course without sponsorship from a member. Do you know any of our members?"

Not to be denied, Herman said, " No, but may I see your roster?" After studying the list, he came across a Mister Cohn, and called him." Mister Cohn, my name is Herman Ginsburg from Chicago and in speaking with your golf pro he informs me that I need a sponsor in order to play your course. Will you please tell him it's OK for me to play? Of course, I'll reimburse you for any charges and when you come to Chicago you'll be my guest at our course."

Hardly able to believe what he heard, Mister Cohn asked, " Of all people, why are you calling me?"

"Isn't it obvious?" Herman replied, "You appear to be the only Jewish member in your club"

"Jewish! I'm not Jewish," he yelled. "I'm Presbyterian. My wife is Presbyterian. My two daughters are Presbyterian, and my mother, *aleha ha-shalom*—'may she rest in peace'—was Presbyterian."

This amusing, but painful joke evokes many questions about Jewish identity: the question of religious status when one parent is Jewish and one is not.

Who is Jewish in the joke? Most likely Herman and Mister Cohn's mother. I think we can safely assume that his wife and children are not Jewish. We do not know if Mister Cohn converted. As you can see, there are no easy answers to these questions.

Before 1984, most *Britot* were done by Orthodox *mohalim* and some were done by physicians with a rabbi who would perform the necessary blessings. There was virtually no argument about who was a Jew and therefore who was eligible to have a *Brit milah*. However, in 1983, Reform, and later Reconstructionist, Judaism adopted the concept of "Patrilineal Descent." The Central Conference of American Rabbis (CCAR) declared that in North America, the child of one Jewish parent is under the presumption of Jewish descent. This presumption of the status of the offspring of any mixed marriage is to be established through appropriate and timely public and formal acts of identification with the Jewish faith and people. The performance of these *mitzvot* serves to commit those who participate in them, both parent and child, to Jewish life.

Shortly afterwards, the Reform Movement started training physicians and other health professionals, including nurses and nurse-midwives, to be *mohalim/ot*. Children of non-Jewish mothers now were able to have a *Brit milah* as an enabling first step in the process of their child being accepted as a Jew.

However, the Jewish status of such a child is under challenge by other denominations and therefore, the *Brit milah* is also in question. More traditional Jewish movements deny the religious status of a child when the mother is not Jewish. What is at stake is, "Who is a Jew?" and the answers differ with each denomination of Judaism.

Orthodox Jews accept the concept of matrilineal descent exclusively, and therefore consider a child to be a Jew if the mother of the child is a Jew by birth or if the child is converted by Orthodox conversion procedures; specifically:

1. *Brit milah*—ritual circumcision by an Orthodox *mohel*. If a male was previously circumcised, but not by an Orthodox *mohel*, he will require *hatafat dam brit* —the drawing of a drop of blood from the remnant of the prepuce as a sign of the Covenant,

2. Orthodox *mikvah*—immersion in a ritual bath,

3. Appropriate Jewish education and/or Jewish experience, if the child is of educable age, and

4. Appearance before, and acceptance of, an Orthodox *beit din* —rabbinical court at age 13 for boys and 12 for girls.

Satisfying these requirements, an Orthodox *mohel* will do the *Brit milah* of the child from such a conversion.

Conservative Judaism utilizes the same model with their own *mikvah* and *beit din*, and almost always will recognize Orthodox conversions. However Orthodoxy does not accept the authority of any non-Orthodox *beit din*, or recognize *britot* or *hatafat dam brit* performed by anyone not Orthodox.

Reform and Reconstructionist Judaism accept Orthodox or Conservative conversions or patrilineal descent which is cited above. However, they also recognize matrilineal descent when, in a mixed marriage, the mother is Jewish and the parents agree to raise the child as a Jew.

Reading the above statement of "patrilineality" brings up the question, "Isn't the child of a Jewish mother always automatically Jewish?" The declaration of the CCAR implies that if parents want their child to be Jewish, this can only occur through a public process of being or acting Jewish. It requires voluntary acts and entails interaction with the Jewish community.

Consider these examples: (1.) A Jewish mother wants a *Brit milah* and her Catholic husband wants a baptism; (2.) A Jewish born mother and Christian father are members of Jews-for-Jesus and want a "Brit milah" for their son. These examples clearly do not qualify for "presumption" of Jewish status under "patrilineal descent" although they are Jewish by birth. If the child is to be considered Jewish, he and his parents must live a Jewish life requiring:

1. *Brit milah*—the ritual circumcision performed on the eighth day of life,

2. a Jewish education,

3. *Bar Mitzvah,*

4. a Jewish wedding, and

5. religious affiliation.

For a girl, they would include:

1. a baby naming in temple and/or a *Brit banot*—naming ceremony for a daughter,

2. a Jewish education,

3. *Bat mitzvah* and/or confirmation,

4. a Jewish wedding, and

5. religious affiliation.

Although it is not a requirement of Reform Judaism, many rabbis encourage *mikvah* as another public act of identity, and it is ultimately required by Conservative and Orthodox Judaism.

Patrilineal Jewish identity is not attained by any single event, but through a life long process and will only be recognized in Reform and Reconstructionist settings, which for the most part makes this a North American phenomenon. In fact, the Reform ruling was specifically for North America only. They intended to avoid a confrontation with the Orthodox within Israel.

So, does a *Brit milah* or a baby naming make someone Jewish? In any Jewish movement the answer is "no." In actuality, circumcision, by itself, never confers Jewish status. For the Orthodox or Conservative, circumcision is only the first step in the process outlined above towards conversion. This includes adopted children if the birth mother is not Jewish. It is interesting that if the child is Jewish by birth, Jewish status is not denied if he is not circumcised.

In the Reform model of patrilineality, circumcision is merely the first public and formal act of identification. At best, it can be thought as an enabling procedure, allowing a child to embark along a pathway towards Judaism. If he wanted to marry a more traditional woman or choose to embrace Conservatism or Orthodoxy, having been circumcised, his process would be less painful.

At most, he will have to undergo a *hatafat dam brit* . This is a simple, virtually painless procedure which is a lot easier than undergoing adult circumcision. Some Conservative *mikvot* accept *britot* done by Reform *mohalim/ot* and do not require *hatafat dam brit in* those instances. After that, *mikvah* and appearance before a *beit din* are required, and if he has had a Jewish education and lived a Jewish life the task will be easier.

Even if the child of a Jewish-born mother is not raised as a Jew, he or she, at the age of maturity, may always return to Judaism.

Obviously, during infancy and childhood, the responsibility to continue along this pathway lies with the parents. Any parent who converts a child knows there is a potential for him or her not to accept this conversion later in life.

According to Rabbi Elliot Dorff, Rector of the University of Judaism in Los Angeles, "If a child undergoes conversion, upon becoming a *bar mitzvah*, once he recites the appropriate blessings before a *minyan*, he can no longer deny his conversion. The family or rabbi need not ask him, at that time, whether he wishes to remain a Jew; simply having a *bar mitzvah* in which he affirms his Jewish identity probably will make it irrevocable."

The best way to assure this will happen is by parents leading by example—having the family live a full Jewish life.

✡

Chapter Twenty-four

CAN A BRIT BE DONE
IN THE HOSPITAL?

When my oldest son was born, I was a resident in urology at Michael Reese Hospital in Chicago, Illinois. Like all Jewish hospitals in those days, the hospital had a *Brit milah* room and many Jewish mothers stayed until the eighth day so that the *brit* could be done before they went home. The nurses loved it because they always got the leftovers from the party. By the time my second son was born, insurance was allowing only a three day stay and my third son stayed less than three days. Now many mothers are discharged within forty-eight hours.

When most people call me to ask this question, they are really asking if I will do a circumcision in the hospital and "say a few prayers." They do so for three reasons:

1. Insurance will pay for the circumcision in the hospital. If a doctor performs the circumcision as part of a *Brit milah*, most insurance companies will pay for it anyway.

2. They think it is safer to do the circumcision in the hospital. This is not necessarily true. Circumcisions are not done in an operating room. There is no greater level of sterility in a hospital nursery than in your home, and there are no hospital acquired bacteria lurking in your home. The baby has had more time to recover from the trauma of birth and his clotting factors are at peak levels at eight days.

3. They don't want to go through all of the trouble of having a *brit* at home. This may be for a variety of reasons including cost, family politics, they are not "that Jewish," or the mother will be recovering from a Cesarian section.

After explaining away the first two reasons listed above, cost and safety, I emphasize that the ceremony does not require great numbers of people or a fancy party. Also, I politely explain that I cannot and will not circumcise a Jewish boy before the eighth day, continuing that if they are having the circumcision as a public act of identity for Jewish status under the doctrine of Patrilineality, that this does not qualify as such an act. Finally, I explain about the probable future necessity of a *hatafat dam brit*—the drawing of a ceremonial drop of blood from remaining foreskin. With these facts in hand, most parents will then schedule a home *brit*.

There is one circumstance under which I will perform a *brit* in the hospital, and that is when the child has to stay at the hospital for medical reasons. On some occasions, this has been on the eighth day (but never before) and sometimes, if the child was very premature, it has been after several weeks. Most neonatal intensive care units or nurseries are very cooperative and the nurses still look forward to the leftovers

✡

Chapter Twenty-five

DO SOME BABIES REQUIRE
A SECOND CIRCUMCISION?

This question raises many issues regarding *Halachah*—Jewish Law—surgical techniques and after-care. I'll present a situation that happened to me in hope of sorting out these issues.

Several months after her son's *brit,* which I had performed, the mother called me up to say her son might need another circumcision. Because there was some redundancy of his remaining foreskin, she contacted an Orthodox rabbi-*mohel* who, without examining the child, said that—according to Jewish law, he was not circumcised and required re-circumcision. She then went to a pediatric urologist who examined him and said that the procedure could be done if she insisted, but that it would only be for cosmetic purposes since the circumcision was adequate. Soon after that she called me. I knew that I had performed a satisfactory circumcision, and so I asked if I could see the child.

I arrived at their home and at first glance found what I had expected. The child was quite chubby, particularly around the area of the lower abdomen, penis and scrotum. The skin surrounding the penis and scrotum was quite loose, as it tends to be in such cases, and the scrotum was large. With the child's legs slightly bent, it pushed the scrotum upwards, retracting the penis into the surrounding folds of fat, leaving only about a quarter of the head of the penis exposed.

Gently pushing down the skin surrounding the penis to simulate an erection, two things were obvious; his circumcision was adequate when the penis was erect and the situation had been exaggerated by adhesions which had formed between the lower portion of the *glans penis* and the skin around the shaft of the penis.

I explained to the parents that if they had seen me at the suggested seven-to-ten day postoperative visit, this could have been avoided. All too often they see their pediatrician who will not look for these adhesions and assume everything is satisfactory. In a few seconds, with barely a whimper from the child, I was able to manually break up these adhesions and then the circumcision looked perfect. Similar to my usual post-op instructions, I asked the parents, with every diaper change for a week, to push the skin back as instructed and put Vaseline on the raw surface during the healing phase to prevent further adhesions. The child healed with a good result and I instructed the parents to call me if there were any further problems.

What are the issues at hand? First, let us examine the Jewish law. After a *brit*, if a baby still looks uncircumcised, he is to be examined with the penis erect. If he still looks uncircumcised, he is to be regarded as uncircumcised. The rabbi-*mohel* mentioned above never examined the child and almost caused the parents to unnecessarily revise the circumcision. They were lucky not to run into a knife-happy urologist. However, he either neglected to examine for adhesions, or chose to ignore them. As an adult, such adhesions can become permanent, obliterating some of the normal anatomy or create bridges of skin between the head of the penis and the shaft which may become troublesome.

My post-op instructions are aimed at preventing such problems. However, even though I go over them in detail, parents are often tired, stressed or distracted and will not follow them. That is why I always offer a post-op visit as part of my services.

The techniques required to circumcise the child described above are worth mentioning. In the *Transcript of the Symposium Conducted at Mount Sinai Medical School, New York City, regarding Brit Mila and Medicine,* Elliot Leiter, M.D., stated to Orthodox *mohalim* what I had known and practiced for years, and yet had never seen in print: in fat babies, as much inside skin as possible must be removed to prevent the "buried penis." This is most effectively done with a bell-shaped clamp of the Gomco or Plastibell variety. If not enough inside skin is removed, when the penis retracts, scarring will occur at the junction of the inside skin and the normal skin on the shaft. Severe instances of this do require revision of the circumcision—removing most of the inside skin.

With chubby children I always point out potential problems to the parents and carefully go over the post-op care with them. However, as you can see, occasionally some slip through the cracks. It is the responsibility of well-informed and well-intentioned rabbis, *mohalim* and physicians to see that they don't slip too far. The best back-up is a well-informed parent.

✡

Chapter Twenty-six

SPECIAL MEDICAL SITUATIONS

ARE THERE MEDICAL CONDITIONS THAT REQUIRE DELAYING THE BRIT?
CAN A BRIT BE DONE IF THERE IS JAUNDICE?
DO CHILDREN WHO DIE REQUIRE CIRCUMCISION?

*Hypospadius** is a congenital condition which occurs, to some degree, in about one in two thousand male births and is not necessarily transmitted from father to son. Normally the opening of the urinary passage tube, the urethra, is located at the tip of the penis. In *hypospadius*, this opening may be found anywhere on the underside of the penis, from the head of the penis to a position down the shaft of the penis, as near or below the scrotal sac. There is also a very rare condition, *epispadius*, where the hole is situated on the top of the penis.

An accompanying condition called *chordee*—a C-shaped curvature of the penis—almost always occurs with *hypospadius*. *Hypospadius* without *chordee* is an extremely rare condition and when it occurs the circumcision may have to be delayed since the foreskin may be needed to reconstruct the urethra. For this reason the circumciser must always be aware of the position of the *meatal* opening before the circumcision.

Chordee is associated with a typical hooding of what is left of the foreskin, called a "cobra hood." This hood should <u>never</u> be removed by anyone except an experienced urologist, pediatric surgeon, or plastic surgeon who has determined that the condi-

* In this chapter we have italicized complex medical terms.

tion is so minimal that a formal repair will not be necessary. The foreskin is often needed for the surgical repair.

Children with this configuration are often called "born circumcised" and questions arise as how to proceed with a *brit*. Typically, repairs of this condition are not attempted before six to nine months, and often one year of age. Does the child remain nameless for this period of time? Since the child appears circumcised, does anything else have to be done except name the child?

There are many approaches to this condition, which has no biblical reference. First of all, as we know, any *brit* is to be delayed if it may compromise the health of the child. Under these circumstances, a circumcision should not be done on the eighth day. Non-medical *mohalim* must wait until the surgery is performed before they can recite the appropriate blessings.

Another approach would be to name the child on the eighth day in a Covenantal service, incorporating *hatafat dam brit*— drawing of a ritual drop of blood from the remaining foreskin— with the baby naming. The condition of being born circumcised—*nolad mahul*—has been discussed, and responses take two approaches as to whether these children should have a *hatafat dam brit*. Some suggest that none is needed, but the consensus seems to be that the drop of blood should be drawn. From a medical point of view, if this is carefully done there will be no untoward effects that will affect the later surgical repair.

Many situations support performing a Covenantal service. This allows friends and family a chance to support the parents and prevents the family from feeling that their newborn son is to be excluded from the Covenant. Another consideration that recently came to light was the fear that elderly and feeble grandparents might not live to see their grandchild named and accepted into the Covenant if they had to wait for a year to pass.

There are other congenital conditions which may occur and beg the question as to whether a *Brit milah* should be performed. The general rule is that if performing the circumcision poses no threat to the child's health it must be done. Such conditions include non-life-threatening jaundice, Down's Syndrome and congenital absence or dislocation of a limb. Scrotal pathology such as large hernias or *hydroceles*—sacs of fluid surrounding the testicle—may be so severe as to make a satisfactory circumcision impossible. If so, the circumcision should be delayed until after the surgical repair. Sometimes the circumcision is done at the time of the surgery with the appropriate blessings, and the naming and festivities are done in the hospital or at a later time at home.

Jaundice is a yellow discoloration of the skin and eyeballs created when bile pigments are not excreted normally by the liver. By far, it is the most common problem. In earlier times it was a cause for delay. After all discoloration disappeared, the *brit* was to be done a week later.

Today, we have a much clearer understanding of the physio-pathology of jaundice, and it rarely causes delay of the *brit*. As a result, they remain in the blood vessels, and are readily seen. The most common cause is an immaturity of the liver to break down these pigments, a condition which almost always corrects itself soon after birth. When this is the cause, it is called "physiologic jaundice," and it is not a life-threatening condition. These pigments can be broken down artificially by placing the child in direct sunlight or artificial light. However, there are other conditions, particularly infections, which may also create this condition. The child must be carefully evaluated. The level of jaundice can be measured by a blood test called a serum billirubin. Most physicians agree that if the serum billirubin is below 17 milligrams per millimeter and is going down, that it is safe to perform circumcision. However, as so often stated, if there is any question at all regarding the child's health, the *brit* is to be delayed.

There are some bleeding factor deficiencies which require waiting until the child can be worked up and observed for a period of time. I circumcised two children in a family, both at three months of age, after medical clearance had been obtained. Both did well and in retrospect could have been done earlier, but it is always wise to err on the side of safety. In ancient times if two children died of bleeding as a result of hemophilia or similar bleeding defects, no other children were to be circumcised in that family. If I were such a parent, I don't know if I would have subjected even my second son to circumcision.

Of course, the ultimate birth tragedy is infant death, and there are traditional directives concerning this. If a child dies before the eighth day, or is not circumcised because of failing health and later dies, he is to be circumcised before burial. No accompanying blessings are required of the father or the *mohel*. It is difficult to ask parents to subject their son to such a procedure after all they have gone through. I have only performed one circumcision under these conditions, and it was one of the most emotionally difficult things I have ever done. The only consoling feature was that somehow this ritual seemed to help put the parents at ease. For that reason alone, I was grateful that I could be of some help during their time of need.

✡

Chapter Twenty-seven

WHAT ARE THE CONTROVERSIES REGARDING CIRCUMCISION?

WHY ARE SOME NON-JEWS OPPOSED TO CIRCUMCISION?

WHY ARE SOME JEWS OPPOSED TO CIRCUMCISION?

ARE THERE HEALTH BENEFITS OF CIRCUMCISION?

Opposition to circumcision parallels the history of Judaism. The Egyptians, Greeks, Romans, Spanish inquisitors, Nazis and Communists all tried to stop the Jews from circumcising. While weapons of destruction evolved from stones, blades and arrows to guns, bombs and chemicals, contemporary opponents have discovered that their most effective weapons are written and spoken words. Today they utilize cyberspace, the print media, radio and television. A network of anti-circumcision groups exist with one common goal—the cessation of circumcision.

Why? Who are these people? What are the motivating forces for such actions? It is difficult to understand anyone whose thoughts are so contrary to what most people believe, but here are a few observations and suggestions:

1. It is easy to overlook the obvious, but it must be said. Although at least one sixth of the world circumcises, it is still considered "the Jewish thing." It would be naive not to consider that some of this behavior is grounded in anti-semitism.

2. Just as the Greeks abhorred circumcision because they considered the circumcised body to be unnatural, there are still some who worship their bodies so much that they, too, hold such beliefs. However, some of these same people tatoo themselves or pierce a variety of their body parts.

3. With the advent of civil rights movements in the 1960s, anti-circumcision advocates jumped onto the band wagon, making it a civil rights issue. Similar groups were formed to oppose vaccination. They believed that children have the right to make these decisions for themselves when they are older. Of course, by then it may too late, and who would choose to make such a decision then anyway?

4. There are men who have been led to believe that circumcision negatively affects sexuality and some even advocate reversing circumcision to improve sexuality. Innovative systems utilizing tape and/or weights to stretch the remaining penile skin have been created. Others actually undergo surgery utilizing a procedure called *epispasm* which was originally described and practiced by Hellenised Jews over two thousand years ago.

If circumcision adversely affected sexuality, do you believe it would have lasted for over five thousand years or would one sixth of the world still continue to circumcise? Do you really think all circumcised men are sexually dysfunctional? As a practicing urologist for over thirty years, neither my partners nor I ever saw a patient who complained of any sexual problems as a result of being circumcised. However, we saw many men with sexual problems from intact chronically infected and scarred foreskins. Circumcision always corrected these conditions. I had one patient of Polish-Catholic descent who kept returning two to three times a year with severe recurrent infections. Suggestion of circumcision was always considered and dismissed. I truly believe he thought that circumcision would make him Jewish.

Of course there are both circumcised and uncircumcised men who are sexually dysfunctional. Impotence is a condition which affects a much larger portion of men than they would like to admit; perhaps up to fifty per cent at some time in their lives. More often than expected, it is due to some underlying condition like diabetes or high blood pressure or any one of many medications. Men not willing to admit such problems to a physician silently suffer and look for something else to blame. Circumcision becomes the perfect scapegoat. Who better to blame than their parents for their sexual problems? It's a shame, because a visit to the right physician frequently cures this problem.

5. Anti-circumcision groups have become more vocal over the years. They skillfully utilize all forms of the media to spread their message. Originally, they avoided religious issues, acknowledging that religious beliefs should be honored. Recently, they have become bolder in their efforts to persuade Jews who are on the fringe of their faith. They frequently submit articles to Jewish magazines and newspapers, and Jews, trying to bend over backwards to be fair, print some of these articles or letters. I have never quite figured out why Jews have to give such obvious enemies a free forum in which to oppose us. When Jews publish these

articles, it lends validity to their cause and encourages continuation of this approach. In one video I viewed, they actually suggested that it will not be long before parents, including Jewish parents, are going to be legally responsible for child abuse and subject to action. They have initiated such cases, which, so far, have been turned away by the courts.

6. Over the years there has been scant, if any legitimate medical data to uphold the statement that there are no medical indications for a circumcision. Much of the data they present is derived from the proceedings of their own "International Congress" held in San Francisco. Few, if any of their conclusions, seem to find their way into mainstream medical journals. However, as a result of persistent efforts, they were able to convince the American Academy of Pediatrics (AAP) in 1971 to announce that there were no medical indications for infant circumcision and that there was no direct relationship between a female's cancer of the cervix and her male partner(s) being uncircumcised.

Since then, medical literature has disproved this and as a result, the AAP has reversed its original position and in 1989 stated that infant circumcision may be beneficial and that parents should carefully weigh the pros and cons when considering whether or not to circumcise their sons.

7. In discussions with urologists and plastic surgeons who perform penile lengthening procedures, they say that a significant portion of men who undergo this surgery are gay. Apparently, for many of them, the uncircumcised, intact penis is the "penis of choice." In personal advertise-

ments found in local newspapers it is not unusual to find the notation that the writer is "intact," their code word for uncircumcised.

8. The most distressing group of people who oppose circumcision are those who are Jewish. However, this is nothing new. In Hellenistic Israel, from the conquest by Alexander to the successful Maccabean revolution, some Jews wanting to assimilate into the Greek culture did not circumcise their male children and even chose *epispasm*—a way of reversing circumcision—for themselves. Doing so made them feel more comfortable at the public baths or games where nudity was the norm. As Jewish religious freedom eroded and Jewish religious practices, including circumcision, were banned by Antiocus, the Maccabean revolution began. This is the basis for our celebration of *Chanukah*.

During the mid-nineteenth century, when German Jews started Reform Judaism, cessation of circumcision was considered, but not adopted.

In the 1960's when the anti-circumcision movements reappeared, a few Jews were quick to join them. Some were mothers who were concerned with issues of pain. I am sure that some Jewish men in these groups became involved because of issues listed above. However, there are some who most likely became involved because of their own personal challenges with Judaism in general, or because of issues of sexuality and failed marriages or relationships. We tend to blame someone else for our own failures and parents are a convenient target.

Self-hating Jews are easy prey for opponents of circumcision. They get a lot of attention from anti-circumcision groups and feel important, allowing them to lash out at Judaism with permission.

Medical Benefits

For several years I have been engaged in countering the claims of anti-circumcision activists by writing articles and letters to newspapers and magazines and appearing on talk shows including the *Gloria Allred Radio Show* and the *Maury Povich Television Show*. There are common threads in any interaction with anti-circumcision people. Whenever I quote any of the established medical literature, their answer always is that either I am lying or the data is not true. They retaliate with buzz words like "child abuse, savage, barbaric or mutilation." Their words are well chosen to frighten and confuse the uniformed and undecided.

However, they have no proven data to refute what is believed by the majority of the medical community and was the basis for the 1989 American Academy of Pediatrics (AAP) recommendations. What follows is a summary of their findings and later data. Edgar J. Schoen, M.D. was the chairman of the commission that studied the data and correctly concluded that there are benefits from circumcision in every decade of a man's life. His pediatric and neonatology experiences combined with my urologic background allows us to survey these benefits throughout a man's life.

1. Thomas Wiswell, M.D., a U.S. Army neonatologist, set out to prove there were no benefits from circumcision. However, in studying over 200,000 male infants he found, to his surprise, that newborn males had more severe urinary tract infections than girls and that these infections were ten to twenty times more common in uncircumcised boys. Urinary tract infections, particularly in the neo-natal period, often

result in kidney damage and scarring. Since his study, Doctor Wiswell has become a strong proponent of circumcision.

Doctor Schoen made another interesting observation. When obtaining a urine sample for analysis and culture, if a child is circumcised a voided specimen or one obtained with a collection bag is just like urine in the bladder. However, if there is a foreskin which cannot be retracted (and should not be retracted at this age), results will be false because of bacteria and debris under the foreskin. Therefore the only valid way to get a clean specimen is to perform a *suprapubic tap*—a procedure where a sterile needle is introduced into the bladder just above the pubic bone.

2. As a boy develops, it is ideal if he can physically identify with his father and brothers. It is ironic that although the anti-circumcision people claim psychological trauma resulting from circumcision, they readily say there would be no such trauma resulting from father and son or brothers not looking alike. When I was on the *Maury Povich Television Show*, a Jewish anti-circumcision advocate said that through "primal therapy" he was able to revert back to eight days of age and he "relived his circumcision." He claimed that he clearly remembered being strapped down and shouting in pain, "Stop, I can't stand this anymore!" Needless to say, my reaction was no different than the audience who laughed and suggested he spend his time on more worthwhile causes.

3. In one issue of the *British Medical Journal* the lead article concluded that too many circumcisions were being performed in England. All of Christian Europe does not circumcise infants routinely, and the rate in England had

climbed to what they perceived as an alarming seven per cent. In the very same journal, a letter to the editor from an outlying medical clinic reported that half of all pediatric patients in that clinic were seen because of foreskin problems. We often laugh about the right hand not knowing what the left hand is doing. Here is a case of the front of the journal not knowing what was in the back.

This incident points out a known statistic during childhood years. It has been reported that up to twelve per cent of boys will have some type of problem with their foreskins that will require either medical or surgical treatment. Some are local irritations or infections. Others are mechanical problems including:

a. *Phimosis,* the inability of the foreskin to retract naturally by puberty. When this is particularly tight, the foreskin may balloon during urination due to a partial obstruction. Treatment requires surgery, almost always performed under a general anesthesia in this age group.

b. *Paraphimosis* which occurs when the foreskin is pulled down the shaft of the penis and it cannot be returned to its normal position. When this occurs, swelling of the tight foreskin occurs and literally strangles the shaft of the penis. If it cannot be manually reduced, immediate surgical repair is indicated.

c. Infections under a foreskin that may result in permanent adhesions of the inside of the foreskin to the head of the penis. If left alone this may impair sexual function at a later date and create disfiguring scars.

4. As a boy advances into his sexually active years there is always the danger of sexually transmitted diseases (STDs). The moist, enclosed undersurface of the foreskin is a perfect breeding ground for these diseases. If the young man cannot, or will not, inspect and clean himself, he may not even realize he has a problem until it is far advanced. By far, the worst cases of STDs I have seen are in uncircumcised men. Although all forms of STDs are alarming, two require particular attention:

   a. During the 1980s, reports from Kenya showed that uncircumcised men exposed to HIV positive prostitutes had anywhere from three to eight times greater chances of becoming HIV positive than circumcised men. It is not unusual to contract more than one STD, and further reports found that the risk was increased if they already had a sore on their foreskin from diseases like syphilis and *chancroid*. These figures have been substantiated several times in other studies and similar findings have been found among homosexual men in Seattle. Due to these results, circumcision has been suggested for boys and men in Africa, in order to control the AIDS epidemic.

   b. When I was a boy growing up in the 1950's, I was told that women who were married to Jewish men did not get cancer of the cervix. This was refuted in the 1971 AAP policy statement on circumcision. They suggested that increased sexual promiscuity with multiple sexual partners was a more likely cause. However, over the years a connection with certain strains of the human *papilloma* virus (HPV), more commonly known as venereal warts, has been identified and linked with cancer of the cervix. When women are infected with HPV, a chronic irritation and thinning of the cervix occurs which is a precursor to cancer. The worse thing about HPV is that it is often very small and not easily seen, particularly inside the foreskin, so a man may not even know he has it. Therefore, an all too common condition may result in disaster for an unknowing sexual partner many years after the fact.

The Center for Communicable Diseases predicts that up to thirty per cent of teenagers will contract some form of STD.

5. Cancer of the penis is a rare condition, occurring in one in 50,000 males in America. No man ever circumcised at birth has ever had cancer of the penis. In certain areas of South America, up to twenty-five per cent of male cancers reported were penile in origin. These are in native areas where local hygiene is poor. Penile cancer occurs as early as in the third decade of life and is a very aggressive, painful and often fatal disease.

6. As men grow older, sexual difficulty and irritation may occur due to progressive scarring from chronic infections. One of the common causes of such infections is diabetes which makes a man more prone to infections in general, and specifically under the foreskin.

I have often been called to nursing homes in order to reduce a *paraphimosis* caused by an agitated patient pulling on his foreskin. This requires immediate surgical reduction. An even more common problem in this patient group is the inability of nurses to pass catheters because of tight foreskins. External condom catheters on these patients are a disaster because of almost guaranteed infections.

I certainly agree with Doctor Schoen's suggestion that circumcision has protective powers in every decade of a male's life. The data is overwhelming and has not been disproved by any claims of anti-circumcision advocates.

However, anti-circumcision advocates—anti-circs—are an impassioned, zealous group who will not be dissuaded by any arguments. I realized this after writing a letter-to-the-editor in *Moment Magazine* and receiving a veiled death threat from one of them. In Seattle, Washington, anti-circs picketed the company that makes the circumcision boards and at a convention where a colleague of mine presented a paper on circumcision, they picketed her and she received a death threat as well.

Occasionally, when I lecture at a synagogue, temple or Jewish community center, I am approached afterwards by grandparents bemoaning the fact that they have Jewish grandchildren who are uncircumcised.

Every time this happens, Pharoah, Antiocus, Tinneus Rufus, Torquemada, Stalin and Hitler are said to smile.

✡

—Books published by the Isaac Nathan Publishing Co.—

- **A Sacred Trust: Stories of Jewish Heritage and History, by Rabbi Eugene and Annette Labovitz.** Two thousand years of Jewish history, from the fall of the Second Temple to the founding of the new State of Israel. Told in story form. 3-volumes.

  Vol. One: The Talmudic and Post Talmudic Age, Medieval Europe: The Middle Ages and the Renaissance, and The Sephardic Age. ISBN 0-914615-12-2. $18.

  Vol. Two & Three Combined: The Silver Age of Polish Jewry • The American Jewish Experience • Our People Return to Our Land (Eretz Yisrael). ISBN 0-914615-02-5. $24

  Three Volume (2-book) Set (from Publisher) $36.

- **A Touch of Heaven: Spiritual and Kabbalistic Stories for Jewish Living. by Rabbi Eugene and Annette Labovitz.** Stories of basic Jewish concepts of Jewish living, compiled by these master storytellers. ISBN 0-914615-04-1. $20.

- **How to Explain Judaism to Your Non-Jewish Neighbor: A Primer to Better Understanding of the World's Oldest Monotheistic Religion, by Rabbi Ed Zerin.** ISBN 0-914615-20-3. $12.95.

- **The Art of Engagement: How to Build a Strong Foundation of Communication for Marriage, by David & Sheila Epstein.** For soon-to-be and just-married couples. ISBN 0-914615-16-5. $12.95.

- **Circumcision: Its Place in Judaism, Past & Present, by Samuel A. Kunin, M.D.** A basic explanation of the ritual as well as controversies concerning this ancient Jewish rite. ISBN 0-914615-07-6. $12.95.

- **What This Modern Jew Believes, by Rabbi Isaiah Zeldin.** The story and beliefs of the builder of a 3,000 family congregation and new 750 student Jewish community high school. ISBN 0-914615-01-7. $15.

- **Threads of the Covenant: Growing Up Jewish in Small Town America, by Harley Sachs.** Ten charming stories of the only Jewish boy, from his Bar Mitzvah until his wedding and the ten Jewish families struggling to retain their Jewish heritage. (A Real Delight!) ISBN 0-914615-03-3. $18.

- **Withered Roots, The Remnants of Eastern European Jewry, by Stuart Tower.** Poetic prose from the travels of a sensitive writer to Eastern Europe searching for the remaining Jews. ISBN 0-914615-11-4. $18.

Continued on next page

All books published by the
Isaac Nathan Publishing Co., Inc.
have quantity discounts available
for classes and study groups.

For information,
contact the publisher at:

1-800-653-9474
(818) 225-9631

FAX (818) 225-8354

e-mail   david@inpubco.com

see our web page at:
www.inpubco.com